Skills for Writing

Unit 5: News writing David Grant
Unit 6: Dystopia Esther Menon
Series consultant: Debra Myhill

ALWAYS LEARNING

PEARSON

Published by Pearson Education Limited, Edinburgh Gate, Harlow, Essex, CM20 2JE.

www.pearsonschoolsandfecolleges.co.uk

Text © Pearson Education Limited 2014
Typeset by Jerry Udall and Tek-Art Limited

The rights of David Grant and Esther Menon to be identified as authors of this work has been asserted by them in accordance with the Copyright, Designs and Patents Act 1988.

First published 2014

19
10

British Library Cataloguing in Publication Data
A catalogue record for this book is available from the British Library

ISBN 9781447948803

Printed in Italy by Lego S.p.a

Acknowledgements
We would like to thank Debra Myhill at the University of Exeter for her invaluable help in the development of this course.

The author and publisher would like to thank the following individuals and organisations for permission to reproduce photographs:
(Key: b-bottom; c-centre; l-left; r-right; t-top)
Alamy Images: BonkersAboutFood 41cr, Capture + 57, Caro 99, Cultura Creative (RF) 11, DavidCameron 96, H. Mark Weidman Photography 37, Howard Sayer 19, i love images / recycling 50, Interfoto 62br, 90, Jo Ann Snover 17, Justin Kase zsixz 34, Mark Collinson 21, MARKA 72r, Radius Images 41r, Roger Bamber 40cl, Vivid Photo Visual 14; **BBC Motion Gallery:** 2bl; **Corbis:** Image Source 89, 93r; **DK Images:** Dave King 41l; **Getty Images:** 7r, Arathrael Photography 97, Brand X Picture 74b, Chasethesonphotography 65, 68, 69, Chris Ryan 75b, Danny Gabay Photography 61, Image Source 32, John Downer 98b, Kevin "Elvis" King 20, Lori Adamski Peek 93r, 101t, Mark Hamblin 40cr, Mark Webster 9, Nature Picture Library 27, Photodisc 82, Sean Justice 45; **MIXA Co., Ltd:** 28; **Pearson Education Ltd:** Studio 8 48, Handan Erek 46bl, Chris Parker NQuad1, Ian Wedgewood 46c; **Shutterstock. com:** AKI's Palette 24, Anders Moden 88, Ian Rentoul 40tr, Joe Gough 41cl, Melkor3D D_53 (UO), 100b, Menno Schaefer 40tl, pryzmat 12, Steffen Foerster 3, 33b, Yan Lev vi, zentilia 23; **SuperStock:** Blend Images 75t, Sebastian Wasek / Loop Images 86; **The Kobal Collection:** 20TH CENTURY FOX / THE KOBAL COLLECTION 54; LADD COMPANY / WARNER BROS 78, 79; LIONSGATE 66, 70, 72l; **Veer/Corbis:** AlexanderShalamov 56, Brooke Photo Studio 36, CLIPAREA I Custom media 62cr, Corepics 8, Elnur Amikishiyev 73, Franck Boston 62t, Ingrid Prats 81, jojof 43, Joshua Minso 38, Monkey Business Images 16, 49, nixoncreative 13, Olga Galushko 55r, photosoup 2, rachwal 100t, SeanPavonePhoto 84, Stocksnapper 59, 74t, tmcnem 55l, Wavebreakmediamicrro 1 (UO), 10

All other images © Pearson Education

We are grateful to the following for permission to reproduce copyright material:

Figures
Figure on page 58 and 60 from *'Gone' ISBN 978-1405242356*, Egmont Books Ltd (Michael Grant), Egmont Books Ltd; Figure on page 62bl and 64 from *The Hunger Games by Suzanne Collins, Scholastic ISBN 978-1407109084*, Copyright © 2008 by Suzanne Collins; Figure on page 62cl and 94 from *1984* Penguin (George Orwell) http://www.penguin.co.uk/nf/Book/BookDisplay/0,9780141036144,00.html; Figure on page 79 from *Do Androids Dream of Electric Sheep?* by Philip K Dick, Boom Studios ISBN 978-1608866151, 29 Mar 2011, with kind permission from Chris Moore Art; Figure on page 87 from *Animal Farm* by George Orwell ISBN-13: 978-0141393056, Penguin Classics (3 Jan 2013), Penguin Books Ltd

Text
Extract on page 2, 6 and 8 from http://www.highbeam.com/doc/1P2-34341209.html, Belfast Telegraph online with permission; Article on page 2, 6, 8 and 11 adapted from http://www.independent.co.uk/news/uk/home-news/top-of-the-drops-keep-britain-tidy-lists-the-mostdumped-brands-8545736.html, The Independent, Press Association; Article on page 2, 6, 8 and 14 adapted from http://www.dailymail.co.uk/femail/article-2302790/A-nation-DIY-dunces-Just-8-young-people-UK-rewire-plug--20-hang-picture.html, The Daily Mail; Article on page 6 from http://www.thesun.co.uk/sol/homepage/news/4836908/Chris-Huhne-and-Vicky-Pryce-begin-8-month-jail-terms-for-speeding-ban-scam.html, The Sun / News Syndication; Article on page 27 adapted from http://www.mirror.co.uk/news/uk-news/tony-parsons-urban-foxes-hunt-1712196, The Mirror; Article on page 36 adapted from http://www.thesun.co.uk/sol/homepage/lifestyle/4820590/ready-meals-sales-drop.html, The Sun; Article on page 42 adapted from http://www.telegraph.co.uk/women/mother-tongue/9986905/Get-real.-Banning-adverts-will-not-stop-children-wanting-things.html, The Telegraph, © Telegraph Media Group Limited; Extract on page 54 is approx. 139 words from THE BEACH by Alex Garland (First published by Viking 1996, Penguin Books 1997). Copyright © Alex Garland, 1996; Extract on page 58 from *'Gone'* ISBN 978-1405242356, Egmont Books Ltd (Michael Grant), Egmont Books Ltd; Extracts on page 64 and 68 from *The Hunger Games* by Suzanne Collins, Scholastic ISBN 978-1407109084, copyright © 2008 by Suzanne Collins; Extracts on pages 72–73 from *'Welcome to the Monkey House'* ISBN 978-0440194781, Bantam Doubleday Dell Publishing Group, Laurel ed edition (Nov 1991) (Kurt Vonnegut.), extract from 'Harrison Bergeron' by Kurt Vonnegut. re-published in a collection called 'Welcome to the Monkey House', Harrison Bergeron," 1961 by Kurt Vonnegut Jr, used by permission of Dell Publishing, an imprint of The Random House Publishing Group, a division of Random House LLC. All rights reserved; Extracts on page 79 and 82 from *Do Androids Dream of Electric Sheep?* by Philip K Dick, Boom Studios ISBN 978-1608866151, 29 Mar 2011, Orion Publishing Group Ltd; Extract on page 85 adapted from Film Education, copyright Ian Wall, Film Education; Extract on page 88 from *Animal Farm* by George Orwell ISBN-13: 978-0141393056 Penguin Classics (3 Jan 2013); Quote on page 86 from Margaret Thatcher http://www.margaretthatcher.org/document/104167 Speech at Lord Mayor's Banquet (12 November, 1979), Margaret Thatcher Foundation with permission; Quote on page 86 from Margaret Thatcher http://www.margaretthatcher.org/document/101374, Speech as an MP in 1965, Margaret Thatcher Foundation with permission; Extract on page 86 from *"Politics and the English Language", 1946 Page 22*, Benediction Classics (15 Feb 2010) / Oxford City Press ISBN-13: 978-1849028363 (George Orwell), Penguin Books Ltd with permission; Extract on page 90–91 from *Brave New World* by Aldous Huxley ISBN: 978-0-06-083095-3, HARPERCOLLINS PUBLISHERS Chapter 2, excerpts from pp.26-9 (404 words), copyright 1932, renewed © 1960 by Aldous Huxley. Reprinted with permission of Harper Collins Publishers and Georges Borchardt, Inc., on behalf of the Aldous and Laura Huxley Trust. All rights reserved, The Random House Group (UK), Random House of Canada Limited with permission; Extracts on page 94 and 96–97 from *1984* by George Orwell ISBN-13: 978-0141393049, Penguin Classics, Penguin Books Ltd / Puffin and The Random House Group (UK)

Every effort has been made to contact copyright holders of material reproduced in this book. Any omissions will be rectified in subsequent printings if notice is given to the publishers.

Contents

Skills for Writing

Skills for Writing is a unique digital, print and training solution. Developed in partnership with Professor Debra Myhill and her team from the University of Exeter, it embeds the principles of the Grammar for Writing pedagogy – trialled and proven to accelerate the rate of writing progress significantly.

ActiveTeach: interactive front-of-class teaching

ActiveTeach Presentation is our digital front-of-class teaching tool, providing you with the book on-screen and a wealth of additional interactive resources to help you embed the Grammar for Writing pedagogy.

Real text extracts introduce students to the choices that authors make in order to create certain effects in their writing.

The Writer's Workshop area guides students through the grammatical choices writers make and the effects they create.

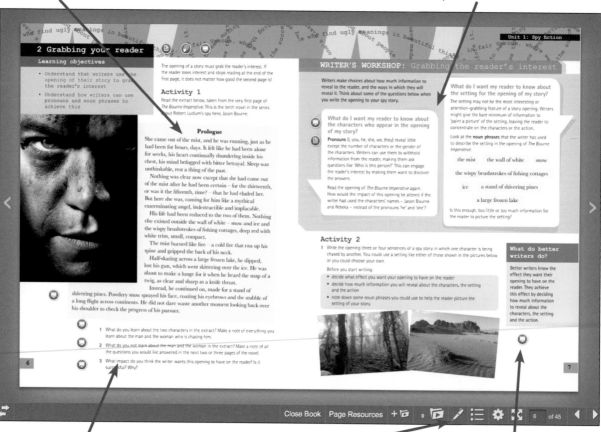

Each page is divided into zoom areas, allowing you to enlarge and annotate each section using the annotation tool.

The annotation tool can be used to identify effective use of language and to record students' responses to an extract.

Hotspot icons link to resources for each lesson, including PowerPoints, worksheets, videos and interactive activities.

Teacher guide

The lesson plans in the teacher guide take you through all you need to teach a Skills for Writing lesson. The lessons guide you through the activities in the student book explaining the effect that is being focused on, providing additional support on the grammatical concepts covered and referring to the relevant resources from ActiveTeach. Extra activities for students needing more support or challenge are also suggested in every lesson plan – ideal for differentiating the learning.

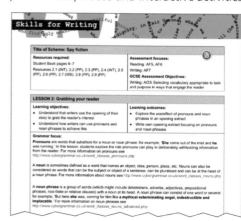

ActiveLearn: online, independent learning

ActiveLearn includes **ActiveBooks** and an **ActiveCourse** that provides your students with a range of independent digital learning exercises for completion as homework. Linking closely to the learning focus of the in-class teaching, these exercises are carefully designed to consolidate and boost understanding and to motivate students to become more independent learners and writers.

Digital homework activities allow students to consolidate and test their understanding of the grammar features that have been focused on in class.

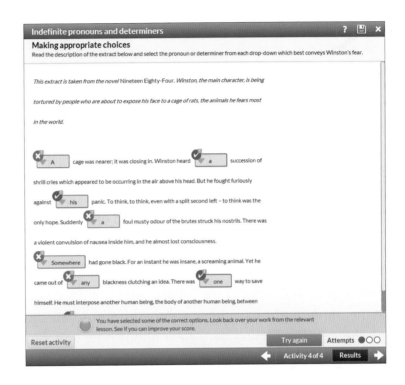

Students are given three attempts at each activity, with hints and tips to motivate them after each attempt.

Independent writing activities encourage students to practise writing and then to reflect on the language choices they have made.

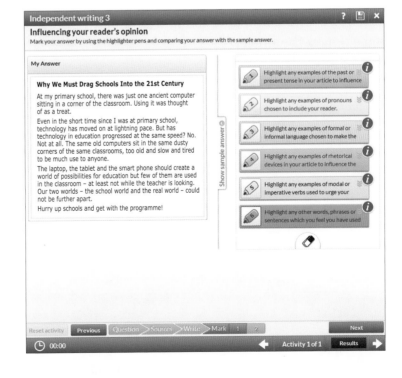

ActiveLearn also provides you with detailed reporting on how students are performing, enabling you to track and monitor progress in writing.

UNIVERSITY OF
EXETER

Learning to write is about learning to be powerful. When you can write confidently, you can make things happen: you can campaign for things that matter to you; you can present yourself and your personality in writing for job or university applications; you can express your deepest, most personal feelings; you can write stories and poems that make others laugh or weep. In fact, you can write to change the world!

This book is to help you become a confident, powerful writer. It sets out to show you how authors create and convey different meanings in their writing by the choices they make, and invites you to consider how the meaning might have been subtly different had they made different choices. The book is very clear about how you can become a better writer, but it is not a recipe book or set of instructions for success. Writing is far more complex than that. We want you to think like a writer, knowing what choices and possibilities you have in each piece of writing, and being able to make and justify those choices with confidence. Enjoy the power!

Debra Myhill

Unit 5

News writing

In this unit, you will explore how news is written about and portrayed, to engage the reader. You will look at the key features of newspaper reports and how headlines are created for maximum impact. You will learn how language choice can imply a point of view and influence the reader's opinion and how to condense large amounts of information. You will then move on to writing your own news report using a range of language features to convey and strengthen your ideas. Finally, you will bring all these skills together and use key rhetorical devices to argue your point in your own newspaper article.

1 Read all about it!

Learning objective

- Understand the key features of newspaper reports and how they engage the reader

Activity 1

1 Look at the headlines below. Which of them might you see or read about in:

- the local news?
- the national news?
- the international news?
- none of the above?

How do you know what is going on in the world? Twenty years ago you would have bought a newspaper, listened to the radio or watched the television news. Now you can also keep a constant eye on world events as they happen, using your computer, phone or tablet. You can share news, comment on news, even make news using social media such as Facebook and Twitter.

a

Top of the drops!

Keep Britain Tidy lists the most-dumped brands

Litter louts are most likely to dump Coca-Cola cans, Cadbury wrappers and Walkers crisp packets, a survey has revealed.

b

DIY dunces

Just 8% of young people in the UK can rewire a plug... and 20% can't even hang a picture

c

Argentinian Cardinal elected Pope

d

Police ram van in bomb plot swoop

e

CelebHotDesk
@celebhotdesk

Lauren and Scott to split! Who knew?! #splitshocker
8.48am . 3 Apr 13

f

The drought that's affecting many parts of England is beginning to have a serious impact on wildlife.

g

Status   Photo   Check In

Michael Blackwell
4 hours ago near Big Sur, CA.

'The Blues lost. Again. Gutted.'

2 Do any of the above make you want to find out more about the story behind the headlines?

a Which ones?

b For each one you chose, make a note of the one word or phrase that grabbed your attention and made you want to find out more.

Activity 2

Look carefully at the different parts of the newspaper article below.

1 Each part of a newspaper article does a different job. Make a note of what each section contains and the reason you think the writer decided to include it.

2 In how many different ways can you organise the different sections to make the article clear and engaging for the reader? Aim to create two different versions of the article.

3 Which of your versions of the article do you think is most effective? Write a sentence or two explaining your decision.

a
> He added: "This survey provides us with a snapshot of what people have littered in communities across the country.
>
> "It also gives 37,000 reasons why we all need to do more to make littering socially unacceptable – to reduce the environmental, social and financial costs of this national problem."

b
> The brands most frequently dumped were Coca-Cola and Cadbury. They were followed by Walkers, McDonald's, Mars and Red Bull, according to the findings.

c
Top of the drops!

d
> More than 500 volunteers enlisted for this year's litter count, which was previously carried out by Keep Britain Tidy staff.

e
> Litter louts are most likely to dump Coca-Cola cans, Cadbury wrappers and Walkers crisp packets, a survey has revealed.
>
> The branded packaging was found strewn across parks, beaches and river or canal banks during a national litter-picking exercise.

f
> Volunteers scooped up more than 37,000 pieces of rubbish in the latest Keep Britain Tidy campaign – more than 10 times the quantity picked up in previous years, according to the charity.

g
Keep Britain Tidy lists the most-dumped brands

h
> Phil Barton, chief executive at Keep Britain Tidy, said: "These results should be a wake-up call that we all need to do more to love where we live.
>
> "Litter is not just an environmental problem. It affects perceptions of safety and costs Government nearly £1 billion a year to clean up."

Activity 3

Journalists often use a structure called an **inverted pyramid** to structure their news reports:

1. Key information
Who? What? Where? When? Why? How?

2. Interesting or important details

3. Least important information

1 Look again at the article that you organised in Activity 2. Does your version of the article follow this structure? How could you change your version so it uses the inverted pyramid structure?

2 Imagine your newspaper editor has told you to cut four or five lines from the article so it will fit on the page. Which text would you cut?

3 Why do you think journalists use the inverted pyramid structure to structure their reports? Try to think of **two** reasons.

Activity 4

Look at the transcript of the television news item below and opposite. Like newspaper articles, each part of a television news item does a different job.

1 Make a note of the job of each section of the television news item and the reason the news programme's editor decided to include it.

2 Do you think the different parts of the news item are in the most effective order to engage and interest the viewer? Write two or three sentences explaining your ideas.

3 Compare your ideas with your answers to Activities 2 and 3. What do you notice?

Newsreader: Now the drought that's affecting many parts of England is beginning to have a serious impact on wildlife. River levels are still falling in many places and there is concern that drying streams and ponds will leave creatures like frogs and newts at risk and prevent some insects from hatching. Our environment correspondent Daniel Bircher reports.

Reporter: A chalk stream in West Berkshire. The bed is almost dry; not unusual in summer but it shouldn't be like this in March. Further down stream, water levels are about a foot below average for this time of year, weeds exposed by the banks. The picture is similar in many other parts of southern and eastern England.

Environment Agency expert and reporter walk along river bed.

Background speech: So, now we're in a situation where all this – all this is exposed to the sun…

Reporter: The latest assessment from the Environment Agency is that river flows have continued to fall at almost all of the key sites it monitors for drought.

Expert (to camera): We are very worried in terms of the environmental impact. We've never seen flows like this at this time of year, so we're gonna [sic] see changes now in the – in the populations of certain invertebrates which will have an impact on the overall environment of the river. So it's not just a big issue for – for humans, it's a big issue for wildlife, this drought.

Reporter: One species of particular concern is the water vole. As levels drop in streams and ditches, its burrows become exposed, leaving it more vulnerable to predators like weasels. Frogs and toads have started to spawn; their tadpoles will be at risk if ponds dry out. And aquatic insects including dragonflies will struggle to hatch in places if conditions remain as dry as they are.

Reporter (to camera): And here's another example of what will happen if river levels continue to fall. Under this rock, the larvae of caddis fly. If they dry out, they won't survive, and that will have impact further on up the food chain.

Reporter: The Environment Agency says it will help those managing important wetland sites by being more flexible with the rules under which they can take water from rivers, but even that may not be possible if levels keep falling. Daniel Bircher, BBC News, Berkshire.

Newsreader: Well, let's catch up with the weather right now. Nina's here. Hello!

Activity 5

1 What was the most important and interesting event that happened to you yesterday? Plan a newspaper article, or a television news item, reporting that important and interesting event to the world.

Remember to:

- use the inverted pyramid structure
- include lots of detail in your planning – for example: who, what, where, when, why and how it happened.

2 Hitting the headlines

Learning objective

- Understand how headline writers choose and omit words to engage the reader

In newspapers and on news websites, it is the headline writer's job to grab the reader's attention and make them want to read the whole article.

Activity 1

Headline writers use lots of different techniques to grab your attention. Look at the headlines below.

1 **Top of the drops!**

2 **DIY dunces**

3 **Is this the luckiest man in Britain?**

4 **Huhne MP to HMP**

5 **Police ram van in bomb plot swoop**

Glossary:
MP: Member of Parliament
HMP: Her Majesty's Prison

Now look at some of the techniques headline writers use – and a list of definitions:

Headline techniques	Definitions
a pun	**A** A shortened form of a word or phrase
b rhetorical question	**B** Dramatic word choice to evoke an emotional response in the reader
c abbreviation	**C** Two or more words that begin with the same letter or sound
d alliteration	**D** A question asked for effect and not intended to be answered
e emotive language	**E** A joke which relies on two words that have different meanings but sound similar

1 Match each technique with the correct definition, then with a headline that uses that technique. For example, if you think that headline 4 uses a rhetorical question, and that this means using two or more words beginning with the same letter, then one of your answers would be: **4, b, C**.

2 Why did the writer of the headlines above write them in this way? Choose two of the headlines above and write a sentence or two explaining how the writer has written them – and why.

Humour engages the reader.

It intrigues the reader, making them wonder what the article will be about.

It makes the reader want to find out the answer.

The writer can get more information into a small amount of space on the page.

It makes the headline sound 'punchy' and gives it impact.

It makes the story sound really dramatic.

6

WRITER'S WORKSHOP: Writing an effective headline

How can I write short headlines that have impact?

Headlines have to be short and punchy because they must:

- be big and bold but be short enough to fill a small space
- have maximum impact on the reader.

One way in which headline writers achieve this is by using **ellipsis**: omitting words that carry less meaning.

For example, this headline:

carries the same meaning as:

Look at the kinds of word that can be omitted:

- determiners $\longrightarrow$ **an**
  $\longrightarrow$ **the**
- auxiliary verbs $\longrightarrow$ **has been**
- prepositions $\longrightarrow$ **as**
- adjectives $\longrightarrow$ **new**

Auxiliary verbs are verbs like 'do', 'be' and 'have', which come before the main verb and add information about time or emphasis.

I have waited for years.

I do love it.

I am still waiting.

auxiliary verb

main verb

How could this long headline be given more impact without losing its meaning?

The local council has decided to fine people who put rubbish that could be recycled into black bin bags

Try taking away one word at a time and then reading the new headline aloud. Does it still give the reader enough information? How short can you make the headline without losing its meaning?

WRITER'S WORKSHOP: Writing an effective headline

How can I choose powerful vocabulary to give my headlines impact?

Synonyms are words with very similar meanings.

For example, the words below are synonyms and related words.

`happy`   `cheerful`   `pleased`   `delighted`   `glad`   `ecstatic`   `overjoyed`

A **lexical field** is a group of words or phrases that are all associated with a particular subject or category.

For example, all the words below are items, actions or descriptions that could be included in the lexical field of cookery:

`boil`   `saucepan`   `stew`   `chopping board`   `recipe`   `delicious`   `sauce`

Headline writers use synonyms and related words and lexical fields to help them choose language for effect.

For example:

Top of the drops!

This headline uses the word 'drops' – a word that we associate with the lexical field of 'litter' – to create a pun on the well-known phrase 'Top of the Pops'.

DIY dunces

This headline uses the word 'dunces' instead of other possible synonyms and related words, e.g. 'idiots', 'fools', 'twits', because 'dunces' alliterates with 'DIY'.

This headline uses the word 'ram' instead of other possible synonyms and related words, e.g. 'collide with', 'bump', 'smash' or 'crash into' – because 'ram' is shorter, more emotive and rhymes with 'van'.

Police ram van

Which of the three headlines above do you find most appealing and intriguing? Why?

What do better writers do?

Better writers think about the impact they want their writing to have on the reader. They carefully consider which language choices and which language devices will help them achieve that effect, choosing every word intentionally.

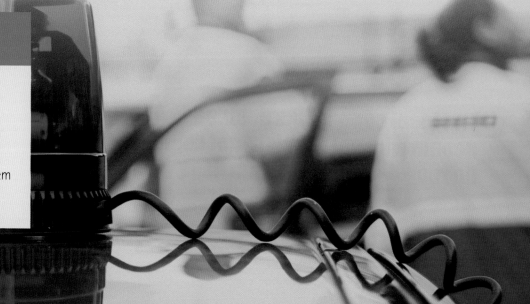

8

Activity 2

Look at this journalist's notes for a newspaper report:

- Man visiting Cornwall coast on holiday with his family
- Goes out to sea on scuba diving trip – dives off boat
- Gets tangled in seaweed – drifts away from boat
- Man's dog jumps in and pulls man back to boat
- Saved!

a Write one sentence summing up this story.

b Turn your sentence into a headline by removing the least important words. They could be adjectives, determiners, auxiliary verbs, prepositions, etc.

c Think about the lexical fields, synonyms and related words you could use to improve your headline. Complete a table like the one below, adding as many different words as you can.

Add your own ideas here

Lexical field of boats and diving	Synonyms and related words for...		
	Dog		

d Use your ideas from the table to create a headline for the article, using alliteration, emotive language, a pun, or a combination of techniques. Aim to make your headline as intriguing and engaging as possible.

3 Getting your facts straight

Learning objective

- Understand how journalists use key information to engage the reader

Activity 1

On page 3 you looked at bits of a newspaper article that had been jumbled up. The article in the order in which it was originally published is shown opposite. Read the article carefully, then answer the questions below.

1 Make a note of the key information in the article by answering as many of these questions as you can:

- **What?**
- **Where?**
- **Who?**
- **When?**
- **Why** and **how?**

2 a Where in the article did you find most of the key information?

b Why has the writer done this?

Activity 2

1 Look carefully at each paragraph of the newspaper article.

a How many sentences are there in each one?

b This kind of paragraph structure is typical of news journalism. Why do you think this might be?

2 Now look at the paragraph in the article that begins 'He added'.

What do you notice about the punctuation in this paragraph? Think of one reason why this paragraph might have been punctuated in this way. **Hint:** Look at the end of the paragraph. What's missing?

Once the reader has been hooked by the headline and started reading the article, the writer still has to work hard to hold their attention. The reader could get bored and stop reading at any minute!

Top of the drops!
Keep Britain Tidy lists the most-dumped brands

Litter louts are most likely to dump Coca-Cola cans, Cadbury wrappers and Walkers crisp packets, a survey has revealed.

The branded packaging was found strewn across parks, beaches and river or canal banks during a national litter-picking exercise.

Volunteers scooped up more than 37,000 pieces of rubbish in the latest Keep Britain Tidy campaign – more than 10 times the quantity picked up in previous years, according to the charity.

The brands most frequently dumped were Coca-Cola and Cadbury. They were followed by Walkers, McDonald's, Mars and Red Bull, according to the findings.

Phil Barton, chief executive at Keep Britain Tidy, said: "These results should be a wake-up call that we all need to do more to love where we live.

"Litter is not just an environmental problem. It affects perceptions of safety and costs Government nearly £1 billion a year to clean up."

He added: "This survey provides us with a snapshot of what people have littered in communities across the country.

"It also gives 37,000 reasons why we all need to do more to make littering socially unacceptable - to reduce the environmental, social and financial costs of this national problem."

…

More than 500 volunteers enlisted for this year's litter count, which was previously carried out by Keep Britain Tidy staff.

WRITER'S WORKSHOP: Adding detailed, factual information

How can I choose language to provide the reader with factual information?

Writers can use **adjectives** and **adverbs** to make their writing more descriptive or persuasive. Journalists frequently use adjectives and adverbs to give the reader more detailed factual information.

Look at these examples:

the quantity picked up in previous years

during a national litter-picking exercise

The brands most frequently dumped were

■ adjective
■ adverb

How can I use language creatively to provide information using fewer words?

Newspaper reports often use **nouns** as **adjectives** to modify another noun, adding more detailed information.

For example:

Litter louts   Walkers crisp packets

□ nouns being used as adjectives
■ nouns

Verbs can also act as **adjectives**.

For example:

during a national litter-picking exercise

The branded packaging was found strewn

■ verb being used as pre-modifying adjective
■ noun

Look at the nouns and verbs below.

- rowing
- boat
- trip
- sailing
- diving
- motor
- sea
- fishing

Each one can be used as an adjective. For example:

sea fishing   fishing trip

□ adjective
■ noun

How many more adjective + noun phrases can you create from the nouns and verbs above?

Activity 3

Look again at a journalist's notes for a newspaper report:

> • Man visiting Cornwall coast on holiday with his family
> • Goes out to sea on scuba diving trip – dives off boat
> • Gets tangled in seaweed – drifts away from boat
> • Man's dog jumps in and pulls man back to boat
> • Saved!

1 Write the opening paragraph or two of the article. Remember to include all the important factual details covering:

- What?
- Where?
- Who?
- When?
- Why and how?

Hint: You will need to use your imagination for some of these!

2 Look at the opening paragraphs of the article you have written. What extra factual detail can you add, using adjectives and adverbs (including using nouns and verbs as adjectives)?

What do better writers do?

Better writers develop their noun phrases carefully to convey factual detail using fewer words, for example through the use of adjectives and adverbs. They also use nouns and verbs that act as adjectives.

CHECK YOUR WRITING

→ Look back at your writing from Activity 3 and annotate your writing to show where you have included:

- key information, e.g. what, where, who, etc.
- adjectives and adverbs to add factual detail.

↓ Look at the table below and your writing from Activity 3. Which column do you think best describes your writing?

I included all the key information in my opening paragraph and added some detail using adjectives and adverbs.	I included all the key information in my opening paragraph and added a range of factual details using adjectives and adverbs.	I included all the key information in my opening paragraph using a range of carefully chosen adjectives and adverbs to convey some essential factual details.

13

4 Undercover opinion

Learning objective

- Understand how language choice can imply a point of view and influence the reader's opinion

The news gives readers and viewers factual information. Sometimes, however, the way in which the news presents the facts can be influenced by the writer's opinion.

Read the online article below.

| Home | World | UK | England | N Ireland | Scotland | Wales |

Video   Current affairs   Blogs   Images   Your feedback

A nation of DIY dunces: Just 8% of young people in the UK can rewire a plug... and 20% can't even hang a picture

It was once a skill we all took for granted, but now it appears fewer than one in ten young people can change a plug.

Only eight per cent of 18 to 25-year-olds now say they could confidently rewire a plug without help or instruction, according to new research.

Moreover, only five per cent of young people would be confident unblocking a sink, while only six per cent said they would be happy to bleed a radiator.

An inept 17 per cent said they wouldn't even be confident hanging a picture, with only 12 per cent vowing themselves capable of using a power drill.

Just four per cent said they could put up wallpaper, and more than a fifth (21 per cent), doubted their own ability to assemble flat-pack furniture.

A spokesperson from NetVoucherCodes.co.uk, who conducted the survey, said: 'In the past electrical goods came without a plug attached so it was necessary to know how to wire one.

'Now though our toasters and TVs come with the plugs already fitted so it seems wiring one is becoming something of a lost skill. ...'

One young man who took part in the survey said: 'I still have to ring up my Dad for DIY help. ... It's not the end of the world that I'm unable to do certain DIY tasks, I mean, if it weren't for people like me there'd be no work for plumbers and electricians.'

Activity 1

Answer the questions below.

1 What is the writer's opinion of young people and their DIY skills?

2 How can you tell? Choose one sentence which suggests the writer's opinion.

3 Look carefully at the sentence you have chosen. Which one word most clearly suggests the writer's opinion?

WRITER'S WORKSHOP: Expressing a point of view

How can I use language to imply my point of view?

Journalists do not usually express their opinion about a news event: they **appear** to report only the facts. However, journalists can **indirectly** express a **biased** opinion and manipulate the reader's response by making careful and intentional language choices.

1 Biased language

Writers often choose language that will give their writing dramatic impact, but it can also be used to influence the reader's opinion. For example, what do these two language choices suggest about the writer's opinion?

DIY dunces — biased noun choice

An inept 17 per cent said they wouldn't even be confident hanging a picture

biased adjective choice

2 Pronouns

The writer's choice of pronouns can influence the reader – and reveal the writer's point of view. Look carefully at the pronouns in these examples:

It was once a skill we all took for granted

Just four per cent said they could put up wallpaper

a Who is the writer referring to as 'we'?
b Who is the writer referring to as 'they'?
c What do these pronouns suggest about the age of the reader at whom the writer is aiming this article?
d Compare the two versions of the sentence below. How has the writer's choice of pronoun in **Version B** influenced the reader? How has the writer's use of the word 'all' added to the effect?

Version A

It was once a skill people took for granted

Version B

It was once a skill we all took for granted

3 Intensifiers

Intensifiers are adverbs that modify an adjective or verb, adding to their emphasis. For example:

really   **totally**   **incredibly**   **very**

Look at these examples of intensifiers from the article on page 14.

Just four per cent said they could put up wallpaper

Moreover, only five per cent of young people would be confident unblocking a sink

What impact do these intensifiers have on the reader – and how do they help to reinforce the writer's opinion?

Activity 2

1 The editor of your news website has asked you to write an article about a new survey of teenagers' mobile phone use. She wants you to make it as dramatic and shocking as possible. She wants the reader to be horrified by how obsessed teenagers are with their mobile phones.

What do better writers do?

Better writers can influence their reader's opinion not only through the facts they present, but also through the way in which they present them. They use biased language to emphasise their opinion, pronouns to influence the reader's point of view and intensifiers to manipulate the reader's response to facts and statistics.

PRESS RELEASE: New Teen Mobile Survey

- 73% of ten-year-olds own their own mobile phone
- 60% of teenagers admit they are addicted to their smartphone
- Over 50% of teenagers would rather give up Facebook, television and chocolate than give up their phone
- The average teenager sends more than 100 texts a day – one every ten minutes

Before you start writing, think about the biased language you could use to make the results of the survey sound as dramatic and shocking as possible. Remember: your editor wants you to horrify the reader! Add some more language ideas to the table below.

Nouns	Verbs	Adjectives	Adverbs
addiction	waste	disturbing	amazingly
obsession	destroy	alarmingly	worrying

2 Write the opening two or three paragraphs of your article. Aim to select and use:

- some of the **biased language** you collected in question 1
- **pronouns** and **intensifiers** to influence the reader's response.

5 Building up information

Learning objectives

- Understand how news articles often use a subject–verb construction to convey information clearly and simply
- Understand how to use subordinate clauses to link information in a news article

News articles give the reader information. They have to show clearly how all this information is linked in order to give the reader as full a picture as possible of what happened to whom – and when, where and why it happened.

Activity 1

Read the newspaper article below.

1 Make a note of all the key events in this story. Organise them in chronological order. You could start like this:

> Joy Grigg went missing in January

Saturday, July 13, 2013

Farmer's wife found in a hedge nine miles away after sleepwalking out of kitchen window

A farmer's wife who disappeared after climbing out of her kitchen window while sleepwalking has been found a day and a half later nine miles away.

Joy Grigg, 50, sparked a major police search after vanishing in the early hours of Wednesday morning. Her husband Richard, 53, awoke to find his wife gone and the kitchen window wide open.

The mother-of-two had been missing since the early hours of Wednesday morning before a member of the public found her in a hedge near Camelford, Cornwall, last night.

It was the second time she had sleepwalked out of the family farm in Tregeare near Launceston, Cornwall, after wandering five miles away in January.

Mr Grigg, who lives on Lower Kyrse Farm with Mrs Grigg and their two sons, Martin, 27, and Geoff, 25, said: "It is so great that she has been found.

"She is currently in hospital, and we just want to get our lives back together and try and get things back to normal. We are all very relieved and are very much looking forward to her coming home.

"We were all very worried for her safety and as time went on obviously the worry grew, although that is all gone now that she has been found.

"She is a very sensible person, a loving mother and wife and we are glad to have her back."

Mrs Grigg was found just as rescue workers were about to call off their search for the night.

A spokesman for North Dartmoor Search and Rescue team said: "We have been out in the Launceston area again today, helping with the continuing search for Joy Grigg. As we were approaching the end of our searching for the day, Joy was located safe and well."

WRITER'S WORKSHOP: Explaining events clearly

How can I structure my sentences to convey information clearly and simply to the reader?

One of the most basic sentence structures in English is the **subject–verb construction**.

(The dog barked) ← The **verb** tells you what was done.

The **subject** of the verb is the **noun** or **noun phrase** which tells you who or what did it.

Another basic sentence structure is the **subject-verb-object** construction.

The **verb** tells you what was done.

(The dog chased a rabbit)

The **subject** of the verb tells you who or what did it.... and the **object** tells you who or what it was done to.

Writers often try to achieve sentence variety in their writing by using a range of sentence types and structures, which they choose for their rhythm, tone and emphasis. However, in news reports like the one on the previous page, journalists often begin sentences with a subject–verb construction over and over again.

Look at the first three sentences of the news report on page 17.

Joy Grigg, 50, sparked a major police search…

Her husband Richard, 53, awoke to find…

The mother-of-two had been missing since…

■ noun phrase = subject
■ verb

How many other sentences in the report begin with a **subject–verb** construction?

How can I structure my sentences to show clear links between pieces of information?

One way in which journalists show links to the 'who, what, where, when and why' is through the use of subordinate clauses.

Look at the penultimate paragraph (the paragraph before last) in the article on page 17. The writer could have written this using two simple sentences:

> *Mrs Grigg was found. Rescue workers were about to call off their search for the night.*

Instead the writer decided to write it as a main clause and a subordinate clause, linked with the subordinating conjunction 'as':

> Mrs Grigg was found just as rescue workers were about to call off their search for the night.

■ main clause   ■ intensifier   ■ subordinating conjunction   — subordinate clause

Compare the version written in two simple sentences with the version written using a subordinating conjunction.

- Try reading both versions aloud. Which do you think sounds better? Why?
- How does the subordinating conjunction in the original version help the reader to understand the events described in this sentence?
- How does the writer's choice of subordinating conjunction add to the sense of drama and tension in this story?

Activity 2

1 There are several subordinating conjunctions that you can use to connect a sequence of events:

| before | after | until | as | just as |

| when | as soon as | once | while |

Look again at the chronological list of events which you compiled in Activity 1 on page 17. Write a short description of these key events, making clear the order in which they happened by using subordinating conjunctions. For example, you could begin like this:

> (After) Joy Grigg went missing earlier in the year, her husband woke up one morning and found his wife missing again.

2 Look again at the sentences you have written. Could they be structured differently, using different subordinating conjunctions? For example, your first sentence could have been written like this:

> Joy Grigg had gone missing once already (before) her husband found her missing on Wednesday morning.

Experiment with your sentences, rewriting them using different subordinating conjunctions – but without changing their meaning or the order in which the events took place. Aim to choose the structure and conjunctions that make the sequence of events as clear as possible to the reader.

3 You are going to write the opening of a short story based on the events reported in the news report on page 17. How could the short story begin? Write the opening five or six sentences, thinking about:

- the language you use to describe the setting and events at the start of the story
- the range of sentence structures you could use to create a variety of rhythm, tone and emphasis.

4 How are the language and sentence structure in your short story opening different from the language and sentence structures used in the news report? Write three or four sentences explaining why a journalist and a short story writer might make such different choices.

What do better writers do?

Better writers:

- begin sentences with a basic subject–verb construction when they want to convey information as clearly and simply as possible

- also use a variety of sentence types and structures to achieve different effects when crafting writing for other purposes and in other genres

- use subordinating conjunctions and subordinate clauses to add rhythm and variety to their sentences and to show the relationship or connection between events or ideas, making their meaning clear for the reader.

19

6 Packing in information

Learning objective

- Understand how to use relative, non-finite, 'that' and 'zero-that' clauses to condense a large amount of information in a text

You can use relative and non-finite clauses to vary your sentence structure, and to add interesting or important information to your newswriting. You can use quotations or indirect reported speech to pack in even more information by telling the story from the perspective of the people involved.

Activity 1

Read the newspaper article below.

14 March, 2013

Is this the luckiest man in Britain?

A man who won the lottery twice, scooping over £1.16 million in total, joked that he was not "that bothered" by the wins and wanted more.

George Traykov beat odds of one-in-438 million when he picked up a £160,873 EuroMillions prize this year to add to the £1 million sum he won in the Millionaire Raffle in September 2011.

But the Bulgarian property developer, who lives in Ilford, Essex, joked that his windfall could have been even bigger.

"I missed the big jackpot by one number," said the 45-year-old, who was just one digit short of claiming £12 million.

Mr Traykov said the thrill of his second win did not compare to his real passion, skydiving.

"I wasn't really that bothered," he said. "Nothing compares with skydiving."

…

Mr Traykov, who never picks his own numbers and always plays the lucky dip, was so laid back about his second big money win that he didn't even claim it until two months after the prize draw in November.

He added that he could be sitting on even more money, saying he had a few more tickets he had not yet checked.

1 a What are the key pieces of information in the article? Use them to write a summary of this news story in just one sentence.

   b How long is your sentence? Can you cut it down to just ten words without losing any key information?

   c Can you cut your sentence down to just five words?

2 What else do you learn about George Traykov and his life from the article? Note down all the information you are given about him. For example: Where does he live? How does he pick his lottery numbers?

WRITER'S WORKSHOP: Packing in information

How can I use relative and non-finite clauses to add information and detail to my sentences?

1 Relative clauses

Relative clauses are linked into sentences with a relative pronoun. The main relative pronouns are:

that   **which**   **who**   **whose**

For example:

main clause ⟶   relative clause ⟶

But the Bulgarian property developer, who lives in Ilford, Essex, joked …   relative pronoun

Relative clauses modify nouns and noun phrases. The relative clause above modifies the noun phrase 'the Bulgarian property developer'.

Choose another sentence from the article that uses a relative clause to modify a noun and noun phrase. In how many ways can you restructure your chosen sentence by moving the relative clause but without changing the sentence's meaning?

2 Non-finite clauses

Non-finite clauses are clauses that are linked into sentences with a **non-finite** verb. A non-finite verb is either:

- a **present participle**, which ends in '-ing', such as 'winning' or 'spending'
- a **past participle**, which usually ends in '-ed', such as 'played' or 'joked'; there are, however, irregular past participles such as 'won' or 'spent'
- an **infinitive**, the basic form of a verb, which usually begins with 'to', such as 'to be' or 'to collect'.

You can use non-finite clauses to add related information to a sentence. For example:

non-finite verb

A man who won the lottery twice, scooping over £1.16 million in total, joked that …

⟵ non-finite clause

How can I include quotations in my news report?

Quotations quickly give the reader a wealth of information by telling the story from the perspective of the people involved. There are two ways to include what people say in your news report:

- You can report their words directly, by using a quotation.
- You can report their words indirectly.

For example, the writer of the report on page 20 could have used a **direct quotation**:

> But the Bulgarian property developer, who lives in Ilford, Essex, joked, "My windfall could have been even bigger."

However, instead of reporting this speech directly with a quotation, the writer reports it **indirectly**, using a **'that' clause**:

> But the Bulgarian property developer, who lives in Ilford, Essex, joked that his windfall could have been even bigger.

Often, when reporting speech indirectly, writers introduce speech with 'that' – but sometimes they use a **'zero-that' clause**, omitting the word 'that'. For example:

In this clause the indirect reported speech is connected to the main clause with 'that'

> He added that he could be sitting on even more money, saying he had a few more tickets he had not yet checked.

However, in this 'zero-that' clause, the writer has omitted the word 'that'

Why do you think the writer of the article on page 20 sometimes uses 'that' clauses, and sometimes uses 'zero-that' clauses?

What do better writers do?

Better writers use a range of sentence structures, selecting them for variety and effect. They use relative and non-finite clauses to condense a large amount of information and detail into their writing. They use quotations and indirect reported speech to tell a news story from the perspective of the people involved.

Activity 2

1 a   Look at the sub-headline of the article on page 20.

> A man who won the lottery twice, scooping over £1.16 million in total, joked that he was not "that bothered" by the wins and wanted more.

Rewrite the sub-headline using only simple, single-clause sentences. Remember: simple sentences contain only one verb. For example:

> A man won the lottery twice

b   How many simple sentences do you need to write in order to get all the information from the sub-headline across to the reader?

2 Look at all the different clauses in the sub-headline:

Main clause: | A man … joked |

Relative clause: | who won the lottery twice |

Non-finite clause: | scooping over £1.16 million in total |

'That' clause: | that he was not "that bothered" by the wins |

Coordinate clause: | and wanted more |.

In how many different ways can you organise the clauses in this sentence, without altering its meaning?

3 Write a short news article with the headline:
Is this the luckiest man in Britain?

It could be about a man who has:

- won lots of competitions
- luckily escaped a series of accidents
- or something else.

Aim to give the reader as much information as you can in 100 words or less, using a range of clauses including:

- relative clauses
- non-finite clauses
- 'that' and 'zero-that' clauses.

CHECK YOUR WRITING

➡ Look back at your writing from Activity 2, question 3. Annotate your news article showing some of the decisions you have made. It might look something like this:

> A stuntman has accidentally fallen from the third floor window of his own flat, breaking only his thumb. Lionel Batten, who has performed stunts in several James Bond films, said "This is the first bone I've ever broken but there's a first time for everything," explaining that the accident happened when he got up in the night to get a glass of water.

| | Non-finite clause giving more detail of his injuries | | Direct quote gives the stuntman's point of view |
| Relative clause adds more information about the man | | 'That' clause introduces reported speech, adding more detail to the story |

| I used some different clause types in my article to include as much information and detail as I could. | I used a range of different clause types in my article to give the reader as much information and detail as clearly as possible. | I considered the structure of each of my sentences, using a variety of clause types to communicate a large amount of information as clearly and simply as possible. |

Assessment: News reports

So far in this unit, you have explored:

- the key features of news reports
- the inverted pyramid structure of news reports
- writing an engaging headline, thinking about emotive language, ellipsis and lexical fields
- using adjectives and adverbs to add factual information
- using biased language to convey your point of view
- using the subject–verb construction to convey information clearly and simply
- developing sentences with subordinate, relative and non-finite clauses
- using 'that' and 'zero-that' clauses to introduce indirect reported speech.

In this task, you will need to use all the skills you have developed so far to craft a short, informative newspaper report.

You are going to invent a news story and write a news report using the following headline:

Is this the luckiest **in Britain?**

PLAN

Follow the steps below and on page 25 to collect your ideas and make the decisions you must make before you start writing.

1 Who or what will my story be about?

A man? A woman? An animal? Or something else?

2 What key pieces of information will my report focus on?

Your news story could be about someone who has:

won lots of competitions luckily escaped a series of accidents or something else

Summarise your news story in one short sentence.

3 What other information do I want to include in my report?

You could think about including details of:

Home — where do they live? Family — do they have one? Who are they? Job — do they have one? What do they do for a living?

Age — how old are they? Hobbies — do they have any that are interesting or relevant to the story?

4 Do I want to include any quotations in my report?

Who could you interview to get some relevant quotations?

The person at the centre of the story?

A family member?

Someone else affected by the story?

And what would they say?

Choose two or more people involved in the story. Write down one or two questions that a journalist might have asked them – and one or two answers that they might have given.

5 How will I structure my report?

What information will I put in my opening paragraph?

what   who   where   when   how and why

Think about where and how you will structure the rest of the information you want to give the reader.

6 Can I think of a better headline for my report?

How could I craft a really intriguing and engaging headline? Do I want to use:

a pun?   emotive language?   ellipsis?   something else?

WRITE

You are now ready to write your report.

Your task

Write a short news report based on the headline:

Is this the luckiest   in Britain?

Aim to write between 150 and 200 words.

REFLECT

1 When you have completed your news report, read it through carefully.

   a Which of the checkpoints at the top of page 26 do you feel you have achieved?

   b For each of the checkpoints you feel you have achieved, write a sentence explaining the effect and impact of your choices.

☐ I think I have structured my report effectively

☐ I think I have written an effective headline

☐ I think my opening paragraph gives the reader all the report's key information

☐ I think I have carefully chosen adjectives and adverbial phrases to add detailed, factual information

☐ I think I have conveyed information clearly and simply using the subject–verb construction

☐ I think I have used a range of subordinate, relative and non-finite clauses to pack a lot of information into a small number of sentences

☐ I think I have used 'that' and 'zero-that' clauses to report speech indirectly

2 a Choose one or two areas in your writing which you feel you could improve.

b Working on your own, or with a partner, look back at the relevant pages in this unit to remind yourself of the choices and techniques you would use to improve your writing in those one or two areas.

c Write a sentence or two explaining how you will improve your writing in those one or two areas.

d Make the improvements you want to make to your writing.

CHECK YOUR WRITING

⬇ Looking at the table below, decide which column you think best describes the writing you crafted in this assessment.

I planned and wrote my newspaper report, including all the key information in the first paragraph, using adjectives and adverbs to add further detailed information.	I planned and wrote my newspaper report, including all the key information in the first paragraph, using adjectives and adverbs to add further detailed information.	I planned and wrote my newspaper report, including all the key information in the first paragraph, using a range of carefully chosen adjectives, adverbs and 'that clauses' to convey some essential factual details.
I used the subject–verb construction, adding some subordinate, relative or non-finite clauses to develop my sentences.	I used the subject–verb construction and a range of subordinate, relative and non-finite clauses to develop my sentences.	I carefully crafted my writing considering the structure of each of my sentences, using the subject–verb construction and subordinate, relative and non-finite clauses, to ensure that I clearly and simply communicated key information to the reader.
	I wrote a new headline to engage and intrigue the reader.	I carefully crafted a new headline, selecting one or more appropriate language techniques to engage and intrigue the reader.

7 In my opinion

Learning objectives

- Understand some key differences between reportage and comment
- Understand how to use the present tense, modal verbs and imperative verbs to strengthen an argument

Journalists report the news – but they also comment on it. They give their opinions on important (and sometimes less important) issues to make the reader think about their ideas and to influence them.

Activity 1

Read the online newspaper article below. It was published just a few days after a four-week-old baby was attacked by a fox in his home in London.

| Home | World | UK | England | N Ireland | Scotland | Wales |

Video   Current affairs   Blogs   Images   Your feedback

Spare the fox, hunt the slobs who treat our pavements like a rubbish dump

How many deaths does the fox population have on its paws? Er – none.

When did we become a nation of total hysterics?

What happened to four-week-old Denny Dolan, the South London baby who was attacked by a fox, was every parent's worst nightmare. But let's struggle to keep a little perspective.

If you want to control the urban fox population then you could start by getting local councils to do the job they are paid for – cleaning up our filthy streets. It should be carved in stone that every house in the land has its bins collected at least once a week. And once the councils start doing their job, we could have a crackdown on all those slobs who treat our pavements like a rubbish dump.

Nobody could fail to be distressed by the sight of that baby in his hospital bed. But the fact remains that the fox population is not kicking down our doors to eat our children. The fox wants to avoid human contact. I live in the heart of London and I spot a fox about once or twice a week. True, they sometimes pause to look with interest at Stan, my Cavalier King Charles Spaniel – is he possibly some kind of sandwich? But their primal instinct is to stay the hell away from me.

We – stupid, slobby humans who always expect somebody else to clean up after us – have brought the fox population to our door. And I confess that I always enjoy seeing a fox. The sight of a fox makes my heart beat a bit faster. It puts a smile on my face – even when they are giving Stan the evil eye.

No, I am not one of those city folk who believes the fox is some kind of cuddly, stuffed toy. The fox is a wild animal. He always will be. But we still have more to fear from each other than we do the fox. And what a miserable, antiseptic, sterile world this would be if it had no place for the wild fox.

As far as I can tell, the fox would prefer to have as little to do with us as possible. He is only hanging around our neighbourhoods because human beings are such a bunch of slobs. We would be far better off having a cull on human slovenliness than the fox population. We scatter our streets with the remains of kebabs, chips and pizzas and then we wonder why wild animals treat our cities like one big buffet.

Save the fox – cull the slobs!

1 a Write one sentence summing up the writer's opinion in the article on page 27.

  b Is it similar to or different from any opinion expressed in the article 'Top of the drops!' on page 11? Think about:
- the opinion the writer expresses
- the way in which that opinion is expressed.

2 Online newspaper articles often allow readers to comment on the writer's views. For example:

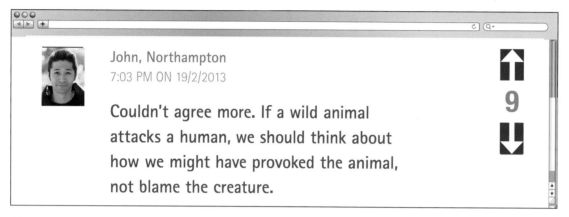

John, Northampton
7:03 PM ON 19/2/2013

Couldn't agree more. If a wild animal attacks a human, we should think about how we might have provoked the animal, not blame the creature.

9

Write your own short comment on the article on page 27.

3 Compare this article with any of the newspaper reports on previous pages. Make a note of any key differences you notice between:

  a a news report (an article in which the news is reported)

  b an opinion piece (an article in which the writer expresses their views on a particular issue in the news).

4 Now look carefully at the structure of the article on page 27. Does it follow the conventional structure of a piece of writing to argue, shown below?

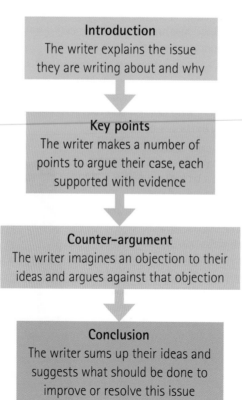

Introduction
The writer explains the issue they are writing about and why

Key points
The writer makes a number of points to argue their case, each supported with evidence

Counter-argument
The writer imagines an objection to their ideas and argues against that objection

Conclusion
The writer sums up their ideas and suggests what should be done to improve or resolve this issue

WRITER'S WORKSHOP: Putting forward an opinion

How can I choose verbs and tense to support my argument?

The **past tense** is used to write about something that has already happened. For example, information about recent events in a news report:

> Volunteers scooped up more than 37,000 pieces of rubbish in the latest Keep Britain Tidy campaign

☐ verb in the past tense

The **present tense** is used to write about a current situation. For example:

> Litter louts are most likely to dump Coca-Cola cans, Cadbury wrappers and Walkers crisp packets…

☐ verb in the present tense because this is what the survey suggests about the current situation

In an article like the one on page 27, in which the writer is expressing an argument, the writer mainly uses the present tense because he is describing the current situation as he sees it. This makes his argument appear more relevant and therefore more important:

> the fox population is not kicking down our doors to eat our children. The fox wants to avoid human contact.

☐ verb in the present tense

Try changing the tense of the sentences above: from the past to the present tense, or the present to the past tense. What effect does this have?

How do I suggest ways to improve the situation?

When writing an argument, writers often express their ideas about how much better things will be in the future if the reader agrees with them and decides to act on their ideas. They often use modal verbs to express this. There are nine modal verbs:

| can | could | may | might | must | shall | should | will | would |

Modal verbs are used to tell the reader how possible or likely something is to happen. For example:

This modal verb suggests to the reader that this is a good idea.

> If you want to control the urban fox population, then you could start by getting local councils to do the job they are paid for – cleaning up our filthy streets.

☐ subject
☐ modal verb
☐ main verb

This modal verb tells the reader what the writer thinks ought to happen if we want to improve the situation in future

> It should be carved in stone that every house in the land has its bins collected at least once a week.

Experiment with swapping the modal verbs in the sentences above for different ones. What effect does it have?

29

What do better writers do?

Better writers:

- are careful to select the appropriate tense to convey information accurately to the reader. They use the present tense to describe current situations and offer comment and opinions and the past tense to report events which have already happened

- use modal verbs to express possibility and to persuade the reader what should be done and how much better things could be. They use imperative verbs to involve the reader by calling upon them to take action.

How can I persuade the reader to act?

Modal verbs tell the reader what might, should or must happen. Commands or imperative verbs are an even stronger way to express what must happen if we want to make the world a better place. Commands give the reader a direct order: they tell them what to do. For example:

Save the fox – cull the slobs! ▮ imperative verb

1 What effect would this sentence have if you re-wrote it using modal verbs instead of imperative verbs?

> We should save the fox – we could cull the slobs!

2 Compare **where** in the article the writer has used modal verbs and where he has used imperatives. What do you notice?

Activity 2

1 Is litter a problem in your school? Write a short article saying what you think should be done about it. You could follow a simple structure like the one on page 28. You do not need to include a counter-argument.

Aim to:

- make at least two key points to argue your case, supported with evidence
- use the present tense to describe the current situation
- use modal verbs to write about what **could**, **should** or **must** happen to improve the situation
- use imperative verbs to call upon the reader to take action.

CHECK YOUR WRITING

Looking at the table below, decide which column you think best describes the argument you wrote in Activity 2.

I generally used the present tense to express my opinion and the past tense to describe events that have already happened.	I consistently and accurately used the present tense to express my opinion and the past tense to describe events that have already happened.	I consistently and accurately used the present tense to express my opinion and the past tense to describe events that have already happened.
I used some modal verbs and imperatives to influence the reader.	I carefully selected modal verbs to suggest that the reader should consider my ideas and chose imperatives to call upon the reader to take action.	I carefully selected and positioned modal verbs and imperatives to build and conclude my argument, considering its impact and influence on the reader.

8 Manipulating the reader

Learning objective

- Understand how writers use a range of rhetorical devices to influence their reader's opinion

Rhetorical devices are language techniques that can be used to strengthen your argument and make its impact on your reader more powerful.

Activity 1

1 Look at the list of rhetorical devices below. Which ones do you already know? Now look at the definitions, which are jumbled up. Test yourself by matching each device with its correct definition.

a Rhetorical question

b Emotive language

c Emotional appeal

d Hyperbole

e Personal experience

f Pattern of three or triple structure

g Antithesis

h Parallelism

1 An image or idea intended to encourage the reader's sympathy

2 Two connected but contrasting ideas

3 Two or more linked sentences or clauses using parallel (i.e. similar or identical) grammatical structures

4 Language intended to create an emotional response

5 A question asked for effect, not requiring an answer

6 Evidence from the writer's own life

7 An exaggerated idea or statement not intended to be taken literally

8 A series of three related nouns, adjectives, etc.

31

Rhetorical devices can have a range of effects on the reader. Look at the examples on the left below. They are all taken from the article on page 27.

2 Which one or more devices from page 31 is the writer using in each example on the left?

3 What one or more effects on the right might each example have on the reader?

a When did we become a nation of total hysterics?

b …a crackdown on all those slobs who treat our pavements like a rubbish dump.

c …the sight of that baby in his hospital bed.

d …kicking down our doors to eat our children

e The sight of a fox makes my heart beat a bit faster.

f …what a miserable, antiseptic, sterile world this would be if it had no place for the wild fox.

g We scatter our streets with the remains of kebabs, chips and pizzas…

h Save the fox – cull the slobs!

1 Emphasises the difference between two connected ideas

2 Adds emphasis to an argument or idea

3 Suggests the breadth or range of an issue, problem or solution

4 Creates a strong emotional response in the reader

5 Suggests there is only one correct, unquestionable answer

6 Adds dramatic impact to the argument

7 Engages and involves the reader

1 It plays on the reader's feelings

WRITER'S WORKSHOP: Creating a reader relationship

How can I use personal pronouns and related determiners to build a relationship with the reader?

Personal pronouns and related determiners stand in for nouns: for example, 'me', 'you', 'it', 'they'.

1 Writing in the first person

In more formal argument writing, writers often try to be 'invisible'. They avoid the first person ('I') and use the third person ('he', 'she', 'it', 'they') to make their argument seem more unbiased and authoritative.

However, in news opinion pieces like the article on page 27, writers often use the first person. It can help to create a more informal tone, suggesting a more personal relationship with the reader.

2 Inclusive pronouns and related determiners

Inclusive pronouns and related determiners – such as 'we', 'us' – allow the writer to suggest a unity between the writer and reader. They imply that we are all experiencing the same problems or issues and can work together to achieve a solution. For example:

> And once the councils start doing their job, we could have a crackdown on all those slobs who treat our pavements like a rubbish dump.

Try experimenting by replacing the two inclusive pronouns and related determiners in the above example with different word choices.

they	you	someone	the

What do better writers do?

Better writers match their language and grammar choices to their intended purpose and relationship with their audience. Using some of the features of spoken language, making informal language choices and using inclusive pronouns and related determiners can strengthen an argument by creating a more personal relationship with the reader.

How can I create an informal tone to build a relationship with the reader?

The writer of the article 'Spare the fox...' on page 27 uses a lot of informal language.
For example:

He uses a **filler** to imitate spoken English:

> How many deaths does the fox population have on its paws? (Er) – none.

Fillers like 'um' and 'ah' and 'er' are typical of spoken language. They show the person we are talking to that we are pausing to think. Here the writer uses a filler to mimic spoken language, suggesting an informal, intimate relationship with the reader.

The writer uses a range of **informal**, **colloquial language** choices. For example:

> He is only (hanging around) our neighbourhoods because human beings are such (a bunch) of (slobs.)

Try rewriting the two sentences above, making them as formal as possible. How does the increased level of formality change the writer's relationship with the reader?

Activity 2

1   Look again at the writing task you completed in Activity 2 on page 30. Have you used any rhetorical devices in your writing? Could you add any to your writing to make your argument even more powerful?

2   Choose eight words from your writing: two nouns, two adjectives, two verbs and two adverbs.

    For each one, note down three synonyms and related words. You could think of synonyms and related words which are:

    • dramatic and biased to influence your reader **or**
    • informal and colloquial to help you build a relationship with your reader **or**
    • both.

You could organise them in a table like the one below:

	Original word	Synonyms and related words
Noun 1	*litter*	*rubbish, filth, trash*
Noun 2		
Adjective 1	*rotten*	*decomposing, festering, stinking*
Adjective 2		

a Which synonyms and related words would add the most impact to your argument and have the greatest influence on your reader? Add your choices to your article.

b Write a sentence or two explaining the impact of two or three of your vocabulary choices.

3 Identify all the pronouns you have used in your article.

a Have you written your article in the first person?

b Have you referred to students and teachers at your school:
- in the third person as 'they'?
- in the second person, directly addressing them as 'you'?
- using inclusive pronouns to create a unity between writer and reader in tackling and improving this problem: 'we', 'us', 'our'?

Experiment with the pronouns in your writing, to make your argument as powerful as possible.

CHECK YOUR WRITING

Look back at the piece of writing that you improved in Activity 2. Annotate your writing, identifying key decisions you made and the effect you intended them to have on the reader.

Look at the table below and your writing from Activity 2. Tick the column you think describes your writing.

I have written in the first person to create a relationship with my reader.	I have written in the first person to create a relationship with my reader.	I have written in the first person, deciding when to write informally about my personal experience and opinions, and when to write more formally.
I have used some biased and informal language, inclusive pronouns and rhetorical devices to add impact to my argument.	I have chosen a range of vocabulary – including nouns, verbs, adjectives, adverbs and pronouns – for its impact and influence. I have used a range of rhetorical devices to make my argument more powerful.	I have carefully considered my language choices, using more formal language to influence the reader's opinion and informal language to create a relationship with my reader. I have carefully constructed and positioned a range of rhetorical devices for maximum impact.

- Understand how to create cohesion in your writing

Writers turn words into sentences, then sentences into paragraphs, and finally paragraphs into complete texts. One way in which writers make a series of paragraphs into a complete text is by creating **cohesion**: this is the glue that holds all the ideas together and helps the reader follow an argument.

Read the newspaper article below then answer the questions opposite.

If you looked at ready meal ingredients, you wouldn't buy them

by Joanna Blythman

Sales of ready meals have taken a hit since the horse meat scandal broke. But a sales slump will not sit well with supermarkets – as the meals prove nice little earners.

In fact, 93 per cent of ready meal sales – worth £2.6 billion a year – go through their tills. So, in the weeks to come, you can bet that our supermarkets will try to lure customers back in with special offers.

That's good news, surely, when so many of us are struggling to pay the bills? Or is it?

As an investigative food journalist who for 20 years has studied the supermarkets' growing control of what we eat, I believe we would all be healthier, and quids in, if we kicked the convenience food habit.

The truth is that ready meals are a con – a way of making big bucks from selling low-grade, low-value junk. So, how does the great ready meal scam work? It starts with the image on the box, designed to get your gastric juices flowing. A ready meal lasagne, for instance, looks as if it's oozing a thick, abundant layer of mince. It's only when you open the box you see the stark reality – a mean little heap of food in a pot.

It's lucky for the supermarkets that few of us look at the ingredients listed. Many people would be shocked at how little of the so-called prime ingredients ready meals contain. For instance, a "chicken dinner" may have just 25 per cent chicken. And even that chicken might have been bulked out already by adding water, oil, starch and sugar.

Supermarkets buy ready meals on the cheap – and this means food processing companies can't afford to make meals with the wholesome ingredients we consumers believe we're buying. Instead, they slash their production costs, using every legal trick in the book.

Rather than using quality ingredients, they come up with something that looks the part but is made at a fraction of the cost using additives, water and low-grade meat.

Why swallow these cons-in-a-box, when you can make healthier, tastier food at home – and be financially better off?

Affordable mince and breadcrumbs, bound with egg, and seasoned, make burgers that take only minutes to prepare and cook.

Now that's what good, cheap, fast food should be all about, not the over-processed, overpriced junk supermarkets are so keen to sell us.

Activity 1

1 Write one sentence summing up the writer's argument in this article.

2 **a** How would you describe the relationship the writer of this article creates with her reader?

b Which features in the article help to create this relationship? You could think about her choice of:

- rhetorical devices
- pronouns
- formal and informal language.

3 **a** Go through the article again, noting each time the writer refers to ready meals. In how many different ways does the writer do this? Make a list of them.

b Why has the writer done this, do you think? Write a sentence or two explaining your ideas.

WRITER'S WORKSHOP: Cohesion in argument texts

How can I help the reader follow my argument?

There are lots of ways in which you can create cohesion in your writing – which will make your writing easier to follow and so easier to understand.

1 Pronouns

Pronouns, such as 'you', 'he', 'she', 'they' and 'it', can help your cohesion. Look at the sentences below:

> So, how does the great ready meal scam work? (It) starts with the image on the box.

What does this circled pronoun refer to?

> ...our supermarkets will try to lure customers back in with special offers. (That's) good news, surely...

The pronouns 'this' and 'that' can have the same effect. Rewrite the sentences above, replacing the pronouns with an appropriate phrase to which the pronouns refer. What effect does it create?

37

2 Determiners

Determiners can also support cohesion by referring back in the text. For example:

> Sales of ready meals have taken a hit since the horse meat scandal broke. But a sales slump will not sit well with supermarkets – as the meals prove nice little earners.

█ noun phrase: adjective + noun   █ noun phrase: determiner + noun

The noun phrase highlighted pink refers back to the noun phrase highlighted green. The reader understands that 'the meals' is referring to 'ready meals' because they were mentioned in the previous sentence.

3 Synonyms and related words

Synonyms and related words also help the writer not to repeat herself and increase cohesion. For example:

> … we would all be healthier, and quids in, if we kicked the convenience food habit.

█ synonym for 'ready meals'

The writer refers to ready meals throughout the article. By occasionally using a synonym, she avoids repeating herself while making her meaning clear.

What other synonyms and related words for 'ready meals' has the writer used in the article?

4 Lexical fields

Lexical fields help writers make their meaning clear without endless repetition. Look at the circled words in this extract from the article:

> A ready meal lasagne, for instance, looks as if it's oozing a thick, abundant layer of mince. It's only when you open the (box) you see the stark reality — a mean little heap of (food) in a pot. It's lucky for the supermarkets that few of us look at the (ingredients) listed.

Which 'box' is the writer referring to? Which 'food'? What 'ingredients'?

The reader can follow the writer's meaning because these are all items within the same lexical field as 'ready meals'.

What other words can you identify in the article which belong to the same lexical field?

Activity 2

1 Look again at the writing you improved in Activity 2 on page 35. Identify and annotate as many examples as you can where you have helped the cohesion of your writing by using:

- pronouns
- determiners
- synonyms and related words
- lexical fields.

2 Look again at your writing. Are there any opportunities to develop your use of these techniques to improve the cohesion of your writing? For example, have you repeated a word or phrase that could be replaced by a pronoun or synonym and related words?

Identify at least three opportunities and make any changes that will improve the cohesion of your writing.

What do better writers do?

Better writers use a range of techniques to give their writing cohesion and avoid repetition, including pronouns, determiners and, in particular, synonyms and related words and lexical fields.

CHECK YOUR WRITING

➡ Look back at the writing you improved in Activity 2 above. Annotate the changes you made, explaining your decisions. It might look something like this:

I've changed this to a pronoun to avoid repetition and to make the reader feel included

Maybe when people drop litter on the floor, they don't think about the person who will have to pick
~~the litter~~ *it* up again. ~~People~~ *We* need to think more carefully about what to do with litter. *rubbish*

I've changed this to a pronoun to avoid repetition of the same noun

I've changed this to a synonym to avoid repetition

10 Image and influence

Learning objective

- Understand how images can be selected to influence the reader

Newspapers and news websites use images to illustrate their reports and opinion pieces. Images can break up large amounts of text, making it look more appealing. They can show the reader what happened or who was involved. But more importantly, images can influence the reader's response to the text and the writer's argument.

Activity 1

1 Look carefully at the four images below. Which image would you choose to illustrate the article, 'Spare the fox, hunt the slobs who treat our pavements like a rubbish dump', on page 27?

A

B

C

D

2 Newspapers and news websites often put a caption under the images they use.

Look at the possible captions that follow for the 'Spare the fox' article.

Some captions sum up the image in a word and then sum up the image in a sentence.

Some captions sum up the image in a word and then sum up the writer's argument in a sentence.

Notice the colon used to link the two parts of the caption.

A A scavenger: a fox raids a bin for food.

B Harmless: foxes are attracted to our neighbourhoods by the rubbish we discard.

C   What a miserable, antiseptic, sterile world this would be if it had no place for the wild fox.

Some captions are simply a quotation from the article.

D   What a load of rubbish: our streets are a buffet for the urban fox.

Some captions use a pun and then sum up the image and the argument using some of the language from the article.

a Look again at some of the caption writer's language choices:

scavenger   harmless   what a load of rubbish

How might these language choices influence the reader's response to the image and to the article? Write a sentence or two about each one.

b Which of the four captions would you choose to go with the image you chose in question 1 opposite? Write a sentence or two explaining the reasons for your choice.

Activity 2

1   Look again at the article, 'If you looked at ready meal ingredients, you wouldn't buy them', on page 36.

Which of the images below would you choose to illustrate this article, and to influence the reader's response to it?

A   B   C   D

2   Write a caption to go underneath your chosen image. You could:

- sum up the image
- sum up the writer's argument
- use a pun
- use a quotation from the article or
- use some of the writer's language choices from the article.

Remember to use a colon if needed.

41

11 Crushing a counter-argument

Learning objective

- Understand how counter-arguments can be effectively structured with careful choice of coordinate or subordinate conjunctions

On page 21, you explored how to develop your sentences with relative, non-finite and 'that' and 'zero-that' clauses. You are now going to look at how you can use these structures as well as subordinate and coordinate clauses to set up a counter-argument – and knock it down.

Activity 1

Read the newspaper article below:

Get real. Banning adverts will not stop children wanting things

By allowing advertisers to target children, we are producing young "consumers" not young "citizens" – children more fixated on purchasing the latest flashing, beeping, plastic gadget, than using their imagination, according to a letter in today's *Daily Telegraph* signed by MPs, peers and childcare experts. However, in my experience, young children are more savvy than that; they simply aren't taken in by advertising. Just as adults get irritated by constant breaks disturbing their favourite television show, so do children.

There's no doubting that advertisers are tuned into making the most of "pester power" – indirectly forcing parents to buy products by capturing their children's attention, knowing that their children will then nag their parents for the latest gimmick. However, surely it's up to the parent to say "no" to their children's demands, especially if they have requested expensive or useless products. Banning adverts is not going to stop children wanting things.

"I don't think that all adverts should be banned", says Professor Barrie Gunter, Professor of Mass Communication, at the University of Leicester. "You could argue that children have become more consumer-orientated than 20 years ago, because there are more products on the market, but it is how parents handle that, that is important. The extent that we want to acquire possessions comes from parents, not from advertisers. Consumerism is simply not going to disappear if you remove all advertising."

My children are four and two and they hate adverts. The second their television programme has finished, they shout out: "It's gone"; meaning their cartoon has finished, the ads have come on and they want me to do something about it. I now pre-record their shows so that I can fast-forward through the ads.

My daughter, who is four and a half, has only ever pointed out two things that have caught her attention from the television: furry animal slippers and Care Bear soft toys. Well, no amount

of "pester power" is going to get me to buy slippers with animal's ears that pop up and down as you walk along; and, from past experience, I know that a Care Bear teddy will simply end up in the basket, along with all the other discarded animals. My son can barely sit still through a five minute episode of Peppa Pig – so once the ads come on, he's up and off – climbing over the sofas or demanding a biscuit. They are not exactly an advertiser's dream target market.

…

Rather than call for a ban on all advertising for children primary school age and under; surely it's better to focus on developing parenting skills. It only takes one or two birthdays and Christmases to learn that most children will cast aside the latest expensive toy in favour of the wrapping paper or a brightly-coloured ribbon. And by the time they reach the age of nine, 10 or 11 years old, parents should have mastered the art of saying no, however much pester power their children muster up.

1 Look again at the argument structure on page 28. Does the article opposite follow that structure? How many structural features – for example, introduction, conclusion, etc. – can you identify?

WRITER'S WORKSHOP: Structuring a counter-argument

Writers carefully craft the structure of their sentences to set up counter-arguments before knocking them down.

How can I present a counter-argument?

The article on the previous page begins by introducing the counter-argument – the point of view that it will argue against. Look at how the opening sentence is structured:

> By allowing advertisers to target children, we are producing young "consumers" not young "citizens" – children more fixated on purchasing the latest flashing, beeping, plastic gadget, than using their imagination…

The writer then adds this **adverbial clause**:

> …according to a letter in today's *Daily Telegraph* signed by MPs, peers and childcare experts.

What effect does adding this adverbial clause have? What effect would it have if the sentence began with the adverbial clause?

> *According to a letter in today's Daily Telegraph signed by MPs, peers and childcare experts, by allowing advertisers to target children, we are producing young "consumers" not young "citizens" – children more fixated on purchasing the latest flashing, beeping, plastic gadget, than using their imagination.*

How can I develop a counter-argument?

In the sentence explored below, the writer accepts this key point in the counter-argument:

> advertisers are tuned into making the most of "pester power"

She further strengthens this point by placing it as a subordinate 'that' clause to this main clause:

> There's no doubting that advertisers are tuned into making the most of "pester power"

■ main clause ■ subordinating conjunction ⌐ subordinate clause

The writer then strengthens it even further by adding examples in a non-finite clause:

> indirectly forcing parents to buy products by capturing their children's attention, knowing that their children will then nag their parents for the latest gimmick.

■ non-finite verbs

Why might the writer have decided to make this counter-argument so powerful and convincing?

How can I knock down the counter-argument?

The writer of the article clearly signals with an **adverb** that she is about to crush the counter-argument:

> However, in my experience, young children are more savvy than that

You can also do this with the coordinating conjunctions 'but' or 'yet':

> You could argue that children have become more consumer-orientated than 20 years ago, because there are more products on the market, but it is how parents handle that, that is important

■ This text uses a coordinate clause to set up the counter-argument
■ This coordinating conjunction signals to the reader that there is an objection to this point
■ This coordinate clause knocks down the counter-argument

And you can also do it with a subordinating conjunction. For example:

> Rather than call for a ban on all advertising for children primary school age and under, surely it's better to focus on developing parenting skills.

■ subordinating conjunction ■ main clause ⌐ subordinate clause

The subordinating conjunction 'rather than' signals that the writer is dismissing the counter-argument in the **subordinate clause**, before the **main clause** hammers home the writer's point of view, emphasised with the adverbial 'surely'.

Other **subordinating conjunctions** that can signal a contrast between the counter-argument and the writer's argument include 'although', 'even though' and 'whereas'. Can you rewrite the sentence above, using a different subordinating conjunction?

Better writers acknowledge counter-arguments in order to knock them down. They use carefully crafted sentences to develop the counter-argument in detail before knocking it down, sometimes introducing their own view with an adverb such as 'however', a coordinating conjunction such as 'but' or a subordinating conjunction such as 'rather than'.

Activity 2

1 Look at the sentence below. It is taken from the article on page 42.

> And by the time children reach the age of nine, 10 or 11 years old, parents should have mastered the art of saying no, however much pester power their children muster up.

a The sentence contains three clauses. In how many different ways can you order the three clauses without changing the sentence's meaning? Write them down.

b Look again at all the different versions of the sentence you have written. In each one, which of the three clauses is given the most emphasis? Is it different in each version?

c Look again at the original sentence from the article. Be careful with the pronoun 'they'. Why do you think the writer structured the sentence in this way? Write a sentence or two explaining your ideas.

2 You are going to argue against the writer of the article, using this key point as a counter-argument:

> by the time children reach the age of nine, 10 or 11 years old, parents should have mastered the art of saying no.

Use the sentence fragment above to craft your own sentence or two. Remember to:

• introduce the counter-argument

• develop the ideas further using one or two non-finite clauses

• crush the counter-argument, signalling your intention to the reader by using either a coordinating or a subordinating conjunction, or an adverb.

12 Planning your argument

Learning objective

- Understand how to plan a newspaper article arguing your point of view

Your task

The government are planning to make some sweeping changes to secondary schools and are asking for students' views on the perfect school.

Write an article of around 500–1000 words. In your article you will need to:

- present your ideas

- argue that the government could dramatically improve schools by implementing your ideas.

Your final task in this unit will be to plan and write an opinion piece for a newspaper and news website in which you argue your own point of view. Before you start writing, you need to gather your ideas and carefully plan your writing. Use the activities on these pages to help you.

Activity 1

1 Look at the journalist's brief for the article, left.

To plan your article, think of **three or four** ways in which secondary schools could be improved. You could think about:

- **the curriculum** – the range of subjects that schools offer their students
- **learning** – the ways in which teachers teach and students learn
- **facilities** – all the different resources and equipment that schools provide for their students
- **discipline** – the different ways in which schools encourage success and good behaviour – and discourage poor behaviour.

2   Now you need to structure your article. You could follow the structure you looked
    at on page 28. Complete a table like the one below, adding your ideas.

Introduction	Why have you decided to write this article and give your views on this subject?	
Key point	What are the three or four main key points you want to make?	1 2 3
Counter-argument	What might someone who disagrees with you argue: perhaps that one or more of your ideas would not be an improvement? Why are they wrong?	
Conclusion	Why is it so important that we consider this issue? Why would your suggestions be so effective? What will happen if your suggestions are ignored?	

3   Each of your key points will need to be supported with evidence. This could be:

•   an example from your own experience.

•   the thoughts or ideas of an expert – perhaps another student or a teacher at your school

•   a fact or statistic – which you would need to research and check.

Look at the points and evidence below.

a   Which piece of evidence supports which point?

Schools need to rethink how they encourage students to behave well and work hard.

One secondary school headteacher, Ms Lloyd, has said that "Students must believe school is relevant to them. If schools are not teaching young people what they want to learn, then we have failed."

Schools must be given the money to invest in the latest technology.

We need to think about the range of subjects on offer in school to make sure there is something that appeals to everyone.

I have had a number of lunchtime detentions and none of them have made me think twice about my school work or my behaviour.

Recent figures suggest that, on average, secondary schools have one computer for every eight students, but that much of the equipment is outdated.

47

You could organise your answers in a table like the one below.

Points	Evidence

b Which piece of evidence:

- is based on the writer's personal experience?
- uses an expert's thoughts or ideas?
- uses a fact or statistic?

4 Add a range of evidence to the key points you planned in question 2.

What do better writers do?

Better writers:

- plan their writing, selecting key points to make their argument as convincing as possible

- support their points with a range of evidence to make their points as powerful as possible

- consider the impact that their points will have on the reader – and discard any that might weaken their argument.

Activity 2

You now need to think about some of the writing choices you might use in your article. Answer the questions below to help you.

1 What techniques might you use in your headline to engage the reader? Ellipsis or adjectives or determiners? A rhetorical question? A pun? Alliteration?

2 Which tense will you write in? The past to report events that have already happened? The present to describe current situations and offer your opinion?

3 How and where can you strengthen your argument with modal verbs and imperatives?

4 Where could you use adjectives and adverbials to add key information?

5 How can you use emotive or biased language to support your argument and give it more impact?

6 Where can you use other rhetorical devices to strengthen your argument?

7 Which synonyms (and other language choices) can you use to help the cohesion of your writing and avoid repetition?

8 How will you present and structure your counter-argument?

CHECK YOUR PLANNING

➔ Look at all the planning for your article. Will the article you have planned:

• engage the reader from start to finish?

• influence the reader by presenting your ideas as clearly and persuasively as possible?

• have a powerful, thought-provoking conclusion?

➔ If you answered 'Maybe', 'I hope so' or 'No' to any of these questions, have another think about your plan and what you can do to improve it.

Assessment: The complete article

Learning objective

• Understand how to write a
  complete article, arguing your
  point of view

WRITE

You are now ready to complete the final task in this unit.

Your task

The government are planning to make some sweeping changes to secondary schools and are asking for students' views on the perfect school.

Write an article of around 500–1000 words. In your article you will need to:

• present your ideas

• argue that the government could dramatically improve schools by implementing your ideas.

Remember to:

• follow the plan you prepared on pages 46–49
• use all the skills and knowledge you have gained and
  practised in this unit
• think about the decisions you need to make as a writer
• engage and influence your reader.

REFLECT

1 When you have finished writing the first draft of your article, read it through carefully.
   Are you pleased with it?

   a Which of the following do you feel you have achieved?

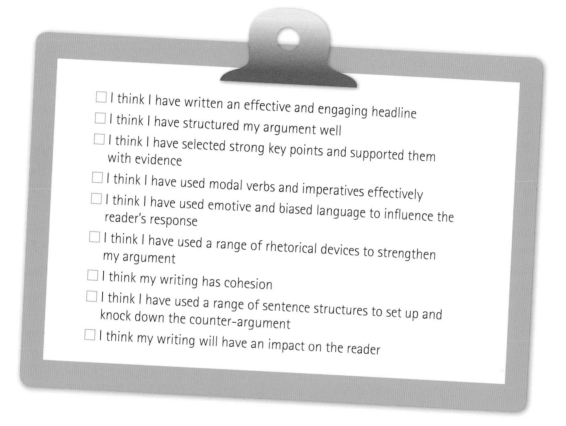

   ☐ I think I have written an effective and engaging headline
   ☐ I think I have structured my argument well
   ☐ I think I have selected strong key points and supported them with evidence
   ☐ I think I have used modal verbs and imperatives effectively
   ☐ I think I have used emotive and biased language to influence the reader's response
   ☐ I think I have used a range of rhetorical devices to strengthen my argument
   ☐ I think my writing has cohesion
   ☐ I think I have used a range of sentence structures to set up and knock down the counter-argument
   ☐ I think my writing will have an impact on the reader

   b For each of the checkpoints you feel you have achieved, write a sentence explaining the effect and impact of your choices.

2 a Choose one or two areas in your writing which you feel you could improve. This might be:

   • making more use of a particular technique in your writing, such as adding more informal language *or*

   • improving a particular section of your article, such as using effective sentence structures to set up and knock down the counter-argument.

   b Working on your own, or with a partner, look back at the relevant pages in this unit to remind yourself of the choices and techniques you would use to improve your writing in those one or two areas.

   c Write a sentence or two explaining **how** you will improve your writing in those one or two areas.

   d Make the improvements you want to make to your writing.

3 Finally, choose an image – or write a description of an image – which you would use to illustrate your writing on the news website and in the newspaper. Write a caption to go beneath it.

CHECK YOUR WRITING

➡ Put on your teacher's hat and mark your own work. Using a different colour pen (if your story is handwritten) or the comments feature (if your story is word-processed), annotate and explain some of your successes.

It might look something like this:

> (Schools should) think carefully about the subjects which they offer to their students. (They could) look at introducing more practical subjects to prepare students for the real world; they could consider offering a wider range of languages like Mandarin for higher ability students; (they could) even think about introducing subjects which would bring more fun into the school day! Whatever schools do, they must teach subjects (which students recognise as useful and valuable) (if they want students to take learning seriously.)
>
> There are (huge) numbers of students at a secondary school compared with the (smaller, friendlier, family) atmosphere of primary school. So it is no surprise that (quiet, shy and vulnerable) students can sometimes feel (overwhelmed, lost and alone.)

Modal verbs suggest ideas, possibilities and essential action

Relative clause adds extra information about the subjects that should be offered

Subordinate clause helps to structure and support argument

Emotive language and patterns of three emphasise contrast and key point

⬇ Looking at the table below, decide which column you think best describes the writing you crafted in this assessment.

I planned and wrote my article with an introduction, key points, a counter-argument and a conclusion.	I planned and wrote my article thinking carefully about the influence that my ideas would have on the reader's opinion.	I planned and wrote my article thinking carefully about the influence and impact that my structure, language and ideas would have on the reader's opinion.
I used quite a wide vocabulary and some rhetorical devices, which I chose for effect.	I used a varied range of vocabulary and a variety of rhetorical devices, which I chose for effect.	I carefully crafted my writing, using a wide range of vocabulary and rhetorical devices which I selected and positioned considering their impact on the reader.
I used a range of sentence structures and used some of them to achieve specific effects.	I used a varied range of sentence structures to achieve specific effects.	I constructed my sentences selecting specific structures to achieve specific effects.
I used some cohesive devices to link my sentences into paragraphs and to avoid repetition.	I used a range of devices – but mainly pronouns, determiners and synonyms – to achieve cohesion within paragraphs and across the whole text.	I used a range of devices, including a variety of synonyms and lexical fields, to achieve cohesion within paragraphs and across the whole text.

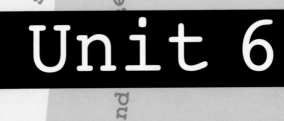

Unit 6
Dystopia

In this unit, you will learn about the dystopian genre. You will explore a number of great dystopian novels, looking at established classics such as *1984*, *Animal Farm* and *Brave New World*, as well as more recent novels such as *The Hunger Games* and *Gone*. You will discover how the authors of these successful novels create settings and histories for their dystopias, explore contemporary issues through fictional worlds, control the pace of action in their narratives and build a sense of fear within their readers. The texts and activities in this unit will help you to develop your creative writing skills to write your own dystopian short story.

1 Perfect worlds?

Learning objectives

- Understand what is meant by a 'utopia'

- Understand how writers can use nouns and noun phrases to create an impression of a place

A utopia is a vision of an ideal and perfect world where everyone is happy and there is no suffering. The word 'utopia' was invented by the writer Sir Thomas More in 1516. It comes from two Ancient Greek words that together mean 'not a place' or 'nowhere'. Perhaps this tells us how More felt about the possibility of creating a perfect world!

Activity 1

1 Imagine you have been asked to create your own utopia – a perfect world.

   a Choose five features of the world you live in that would have to change or be eliminated.

   b List five features of your perfect day in the utopia you have imagined.

Activity 2

1 Read the extract below.

Below is a backpacker's vision of a kind of paradise, a secret beach rumoured to be found on one of the islands of Thailand. The extract is taken from the novel The Beach.

Think about a lagoon, hidden from the sea and passing boats by a high, curving wall of rock. Then imagine white sands and coral gardens never damaged by dynamite fishing or trawling nets. Freshwater falls scatter the island, surrounded by jungle – not the forests of inland Thailand, but jungle. Canopies three levels deep, plants untouched for a thousand years, strangely coloured birds and monkeys in the trees.

On the white sands, fishing in the coral gardens, a select community of travellers pass the months. They leave if they want to, they return, the beach never changes.

'Select?' I asked quietly, as if talking through a dream. Zeph's vision had entirely consumed me.

'Select,' he replied. 'Word of mouth passes on the location to a lucky few.'

'It's paradise,' Sammy murmured. 'It's Eden.'

'Eden,' Zeph agreed, 'is how it sounds.'

2 Look carefully at the description of the island in the extract.
What impression do you get of the island from this opening?

3 a Use the scale below to rate how perfect or imperfect you find the island.

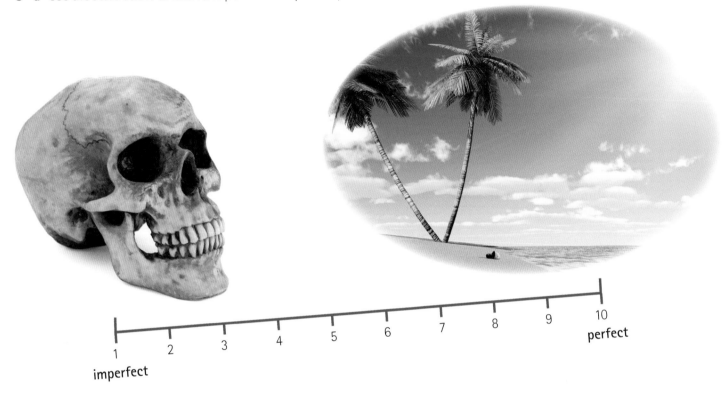

```
  |----|----|----|----|----|----|----|----|----|----|
  1    2    3    4    5    6    7    8    9    10
                                             perfect
imperfect
```

b Write two or three sentences explaining your rating. Use examples of language from
the extract to support your explanation.

WRITER'S WORKSHOP: Describing a setting

How can I give the reader a sense of the setting in a story?

Writers sometimes use descriptive **adjectives** to paint a picture of a setting in a story. However, they have to think carefully about the **nouns** they choose.

How do I choose nouns to create a sense of place?

Nouns are the words we use to identify people, places, objects or ideas. For example:

| lagoons | sands | birds | canopies |

These four nouns immediately create an image in the reader's mind. The writer has focused on these (and other) elements to establish one of the novel's characters and the novel's setting. What impression of the setting do the nouns give you?

WRITER'S WORKSHOP: Describing a setting

How can I use noun phrases to influence the reader's response to a setting?

The writer can develop the reader's sense of setting by adding words connected to the nouns and creating noun phrases. Look at the noun phrases below:

a lagoon, hidden from the sea and passing boats by a high, curving wall of rock

The writer has used this non-finite clause to add descriptive information about the secrecy of the lagoon.

plants untouched for a thousand years

The writer has used this non-finite clause within the noun phrase to emphasise how the island is like eden.

strangely coloured birds

The writer has used this adverb and adjective to highlight the exoticness of the birds on the island.

How do the writer's choices of adverb, adjective and non-finite clauses to add description affect your response to the nouns the writer has used?

Activity 3

The writer uses **nouns** and **noun phrases** in the extract from *The Beach* to describe the different features of the island and establish the setting of the novel in the reader's mind.

1   Identify as many of these nouns and noun phrases in the extract on page 54 as you can. Note them down in a table like the one below.

Appealing	Neutral	Unappealing
white sands coral gardens		dynamite fishing

2   Look at the nouns and noun phrases you have found. How do you think the speaker, Zeph, wants his listeners to respond to his description of the island? Is it a kind of utopia?

3   We know that a perfect place can be described as a utopia. The word for a place that is imperfect is 'dystopia'.

   a   Read the following text from the blurb for *The Beach*.

> The Beach is a legend among young travellers in Thailand: a secret island paradise where a select community lives in blissful isolation. Richard sets out in search of adventure, but finds that the Beach is not what it seems. Paradise comes at a price.

   b   Rewrite the passage on page 54, hinting that all is not as perfect as it seems. Think about your choice of nouns and noun phrases.

   c   Highlight the words and phrases you have changed in the text. What effect will these changes have on the reader?

2 Imperfect perfection

Learning objective

- Understand how writers can use adverbs, adverbial phrases and sentence length to control the pace of action in a narrative

On pages 54 and 55 you learnt about the idea of utopia: a world that is perfect in every way. However, writers often portray societies or worlds that are far from perfect – places where everything seems to have gone wrong. These are called 'dystopias'.

Activity 1

In the book *Gone*, the author Michael Grant describes a world with no adults – a perfect world, you might think! However, it is far from being a perfect world.

1 Read the text below. It is one student's summary of the book's opening.

> This book is about a strange series of events in a small town in southern California when all the people over the age of fifteen disappear. Unexplained events take place starting with a car crash, then a house burning down and finally the breakdown of all means of communication. Isolated from the rest of the world, people begin to panic. The book is about how people form groups to survive, either by behaving in a kind and humane way, or by being cruel and ruthless.

2 Now read the book's blurb on the right. It was written to encourage new readers to buy the book.

3 Compare the quotations below, taken from the student's summary and the book blurb.

> The book is about how people form groups to survive, either by behaving in a kind and humane way, or by being cruel and ruthless.

> Gangs begin to form. Sides are chosen – strong or weak. Cruel or humane.

a Which do you think makes the book sound more exciting?

b Look carefully at the text which you feel is more exciting. How has the writer suggested that the novel is set in a world of fear and danger?

One minute the teacher was there, the next, he was gone. There. Gone.

In the blink of an eye all the adults disappear in a small town in southern California and no one knows why. First a car crash; a house up in flames; then a complete communication meltdown…

Suddenly cut off from the outside world, those that are left are trapped, and there's no help on the way. They must do all they can to survive. Chaos rules the streets. Gangs begin to form. Sides are chosen – strong or weak. Cruel or humane.

A new world order is rising, and, even scarier, some survivors have power – power that no one has ever seen before…

GONE

58

WRITER'S WORKSHOP: Creating a sense of drama

Writers of dystopias make a range of choices to create a sudden transformation: a world that is changing almost beyond recognition.

How can I use adverbs and adverbial phrases to give the reader a sense of a rapidly changing world?

You can use **adverbs** and **adverbial phrases** to add more information about a verb or an adjective. They are a great way of adding detail to a text and can appear almost anywhere in a sentence. Adverbs and adverbial phrases can give information about:

- the **order** in which events take place:

First a car crash; a house up in flames; then a complete communication meltdown…

- **when** or **how quickly** the action is taking place:

Suddenly cut off from the outside world, those that are left are trapped.

In the blink of an eye all the adults disappear in a small town in southern California and no one knows why.

    adverbs related to time   adverbial phrase which helps to show manner   adverb related to manner

Why do you think the writer chose to place the adverb or adverbial phrase at the beginning of these sentences? Where else could they be positioned in the sentences? How would this change their effect on the reader?

How can I structure my sentences to create a sense of drama?

You can use **sentence structure** to create a fast-moving, dramatic pace in your writing. For example, look at the sentences in the second paragraph of the book blurb.

> Chaos rules the streets. Gangs begin to form. Sides are chosen – strong or weak.

> Suddenly cut off from the outside world, those that are left are trapped, and there's no help on the way. They must do all they can to survive. ←

These longer **complex sentences** explain the situation to the reader.

The writer then uses three short **simple sentences** to describe the sudden and dramatic changes in the world of the novel.

> Cruel or humane.

Finally, the writer uses a **minor sentence** – a sentence which contains no verb – to emphasise the stark choice which people face in this desperate and dangerous new world.

Practise reading this second paragraph of the blurb aloud to make it sound as dramatic as possible. How does the sentence structure help to make it sound dramatic?

What do better writers do?

Better writers:

- use adverbs and adverbial phrases to signal in what order, or when, or how quickly events take place. They can use them to control the pace of the action in a narrative.

- control the pace of their writing through their choice of sentence structure. They can use short simple sentences to create a sense of sudden and dramatic change. They can use minor sentences to emphasise a dramatic idea or moment in the story.

Activity 2

1 Look carefully at the sentences used in the student's summary of the book opening from Activity 1 (page 58). How are they different from the book blurb?

2 Can you find any other specific words and phrases in the book blurb that are used to engage new readers? Look particularly for words that add pace by focusing on time.

Activity 3

Look again at the sentences from the blurb of *Gone*, below.

> In the blink of an eye all the adults disappear in a small town in southern California and no one knows why.

> A new world order is rising, and, even scarier, some survivors have power – power that no one has ever seen before…

1 Try experimenting with the sentences by:

   a adding or removing adverbs or adverbial phrases

   b restructuring each sentence as a sequence of simple and/or minor sentences.

   In how many different ways can you rewrite them?

2 Look at the changes you have made to the sentences. Annotate your sentences to show:

   a the changes you have made

   b the different effects your changes have made to their impact or meaning for the reader.

3 Plan a story in which a character wakes up one morning and finds a suddenly and dramatically changed world. Decide:

   a what has changed

   b how this change affects the main character and the people they are close to.

4 Write a dramatic blurb to tempt readers to read the story you have planned. You could use:

   • adverbs and adverbial phrases to suggest the sudden and dramatic change
   • short simple sentences to explain the consequences of the change
   • minor sentences to focus the reader on the impact of this change.

CHECK YOUR WRITING

➡ Read your blurb aloud with a partner. Discuss what is good about your blurb and what could be improved.

   • Does it sound dramatic?
   • Have you used adverbs, adverbial phrases and different sentence structures to create or highlight sudden and dramatic change?

➡ Write one or two sentences reflecting on what you have done well and one or two sentences about what you might be able to improve, and how.

➡ Re-draft your blurb, making the improvements you want to make to your writing.

3 Dystopian worlds

Learning objective

- Understand the features of a dystopian narrative

In this lesson you will consider some of the typical features of the dystopian genre.

Activity 1

1 Read the summaries below. They describe four different novels in the dystopian genre.

A literary genre is a group of texts that share some common features. For example, detective stories usually feature:

a detective

a criminal

a crime

a final unravelling of the mystery

1984
by George Orwell

Winston Smith lives in Airstrip One (formerly known as Great Britain), a province of Oceania (formerly known as Europe). Following a global nuclear war, Oceania is ruled by The Party, led by a mysterious dictator known as Big Brother, who keeps the people under constant surveillance, watching their every move, listening to their every word and monitoring their every thought. Can Winston Smith rebel against Big Brother's oppression and survive?

The Death of Grass
by John Christopher

A new virus destroys all types of grass, wiping out rice, wheat and barley crops and engulfing the world in terrifying famine. As civilisation starts to fall apart and news spreads of government plans to manage the population by bombing major cities, John Custance and Roger Buckley make a desperate attempt to flee London and move their families to safety.

The Hunger Games
by Suzanne Collins

16-year-old Katniss Everdeen lives in District 12 of the nation Panem, where the countries of North America existed before an apocalyptic event ended civilisation as we know it. Each year, as punishment for a previous rebellion, the ruling 'Capitol' organises an event in which one boy and one girl from each of the 12 Districts of Panem are selected at random to compete in a televised and brutal battle to the death.

Brave New World
by Aldous Huxley

London, 2534. The World Controllers have created the ideal society in which humans are no longer born but grown and where genetic engineering ensures all citizens know what to think and feel and how to act. Everyone is happy except Bernard Marx. Visiting one of the few remaining Savage Reservations, where the old life continues, he starts off a chain of events with profound consequences.

2   Can you identify any common features in these dystopian novels? Make a list of what
    you think the common features of a dystopian novel might be. You could think about
    some of the suggestions below and add your own ideas, based on what you have read in
    the four summaries.

deceit	power and politics	a crime	heroes
extraterrestrial beings	the supernatural	conflict	a possible future
scientific progress	a ghost	a happy ending	science and nature
a murder	society	a spy	love

3   Writers of dystopian fiction often take their ideas from something that they think is a problem in
    today's world. They use their story to explore how the problem might develop further in a possible
    future world if we do nothing about it.

    a   Look again at the four summaries of dystopian novels opposite. What problems might have
        inspired the writers of these stories to imagine these dystopian futures?

    b   Choose one of the novels summarised opposite. How has the writer taken one of the features
        you identified in question 2 and developed it into a dystopian world of the future?

    c   Look again at each novel summary opposite. What effect do you think each of the four writers
        wanted to have on the reader? Write two or three sentences explaining your ideas. Use evidence
        from the summaries to support your comments.

Activity 2

1   You are going to gather and plan your ideas for a dystopian story.

    a   What worries you about the world in which you live? List two or three ideas and choose one
        that might help you create a dystopian story.

    b   How might your chosen problem develop in a dystopian future? Use the summaries of dystopian
        novels to inspire you.

    c   Who will be the central character or characters in your dystopian story? What problems must
        they face in your dystopian future? How will they overcome these problems?

4 Building the past

Learning objective

- Understand how writers use nouns and noun phrases to influence the reader's view of a fictional world

Activity 1

The Hunger Games by Suzanne Collins is the first of a series of novels set in a disturbing, future North America. Read the extract from Chapter 1 of *The Hunger Games* on the right.

New York Times Bestselling Author
SUZANNE COLLINS

One common feature of dystopian stories is the idea of a disturbing present day which has come about due to terrifying events in the past: a time when the world we once knew came to an end and everything changed.

It is the day of the Reaping, when the mayor announces which teenagers will fight to the death in the Hunger Games. The novel's narrator, Katniss Everdeen, is standing in the crowd that has gathered to hear the mayor speak.

Just as the clock strikes two, the mayor steps up to the podium and begins to read. It's the same story every year. He tells of the history of Panem, the country that rose up out of the ashes of a place that was once called North America. He lists the disasters, the droughts, the storms, the fires, the encroaching seas that swallowed up so much of the land, the brutal war for what little sustenance remained. The result was Panem, a shining Capitol ringed by thirteen districts, which brought peace and prosperity to its citizens. Then came the Dark Days, the uprising of the districts against the Capitol. Twelve were defeated, the thirteenth obliterated. The Treaty of Treason gave us new laws to guarantee peace and, as our yearly reminder that the Dark Days must never be repeated, it gave us the Hunger Games.

The rules of the Hunger Games are simple. In punishment for the uprising, each of the twelve districts must provide one girl and one boy, called tributes, to participate. The twenty-four tributes will be imprisoned in a vast outdoor arena that could hold anything from a burning desert to a frozen wasteland. Over a period of several weeks, the competitors must fight to the death. The last tribute standing wins.

1 Make a timeline or list of the events which the mayor describes in the extract opposite. It might begin like this:

• *North America is hit by a series of natural disasters*

2 What impression has the writer given you of the dystopian world in which the novel is set? Choose some examples from the extract to support your comments.

WRITER'S WORKSHOP: Manipulating the reader's response

One of the writer's purposes in the extract opposite is to give the reader the novel's back-story. A back-story is the background information which the reader needs in order to understand the dystopian setting of the novel.

However, the writer has also carefully selected the language of the back-story to influence the reader's response to this society, its rulers and its victims.

In the *Hunger Games* extract, the writer uses three different forms of noun phrase (short, expanded and proper) to describe three different stages in the history of Panem.

How can I use short noun phrases to influence the reader's response to my dystopian world?

The mayor describes the natural disasters and the war that destroyed North America:

the disasters, the droughts, the storms the fires,   the brutal war

The writer first uses a number of short noun phrases to suggest a time of relentless chaos.

The writer completes the list with a longer noun phrase that includes an adjective modifying the noun 'war' to emphasise its violence.

How can I use expanded noun phrases to influence the reader's response to my dystopian world?

The mayor describes the creation of Panem in one expanded noun phrase. He compares Panem to a phoenix, a mythical bird that dies and is born again from fire:

> Panem, the country that rose up out of the ashes of a place that was once called North America

▮ This relative clause is part of the noun phrase and adds information about the history of Panem by modifying the noun 'country'. It allows the writer to add extra detail about the dystopian world and its history in a concise way.

The mayor also describes the benefits that the creation of Panem has brought with another expanded noun phrase:

> Panem, a shining Capitol ringed by thirteen districts, which brought peace and prosperity to its citizens.

The noun 'Capitol' is:

▮ pre-modified with this adjective

▮ post-modified with this non-finite clause

The noun 'Panem' is:

▮ post-modified with this relative clause

Look closely at the noun phrases the writer has crafted. What do they suggest about the country of Panem?

How can I use proper noun phrases to influence the reader's response to my dystopian world?

Finally, the mayor describes the uprising which threatened Panem:

> Then came the Dark Days, the uprising of the districts against the Capitol. Twelve were defeated, the thirteenth obliterated. The Treaty of Treason gave us new laws to guarantee peace and, as our yearly reminder that the Dark Days must never be repeated, it gave us the Hunger Games.

▮ noun phrases including proper nouns

The writer has used a lot of **proper noun phrases** here to describe this stage in Panem's history.

a Why do you think the writer has done this?

b What does each of the proper noun phrases the writer has chosen suggest about these events?

Activity 2

1 Look back at the ideas you developed in Activity 2 on page 63.

a What has happened between now and the future you have imagined? Create a timeline or bullet list, identifying key events in the history of your future dystopian society.

b Write a paragraph describing the sequence of events you have imagined. You could experiment with some of the choices which Suzanne Collins made in the extract from *The Hunger Games*; for example:

- lists of short noun phrases to suggest a series of consecutive events
- longer noun phrases to describe events, using:
  o adjectives to pre-modify nouns
  o relative clauses to post-modify nouns
  o non-finite clauses to pre- or post-modify nouns.
- proper nouns to suggest that these are real events in the history of a real place.

What do better writers do?

Better writers:

- choose their nouns carefully to influence the reader's response
- expand noun phrases with adjectives and relative and non-finite clauses to give the reader detailed information about the fictional world they have imagined
- use this detailed information along with proper nouns to name characters and key events in the history of that fictional world and so create an illusion of reality.

CHECK YOUR WRITING

Look back at the paragraph you wrote in Activity 2. Annotate your extract to explain some of the decisions you have made. It might look something like this:

Ever since The Disaster, we have lived in the Underground City. The Leader tells us about the Days of Light when we lived on the earth, not in it. The smoke, pollution, heat, the dust and the stench. Burned by the sun, frozen in ice and snow, starved and slowly wasting, our people began to die until the Leader made them dig down into the earth and build the Underground City.

I've used a list of nouns and short noun phrases to suggest the poor state of the environment.

This series of non-finite clauses modifies the noun 'people', building a detailed description of the conditions they lived in before they moved underground.

These proper nouns make my dystopian world sound more real.

Which column best describes your use of nouns and noun phrases?

I chose some nouns to influence the reader's response to my description.	I chose all of the nouns in my writing thinking about their effect on the reader's response.	I selected nouns and structured the noun phrases in my sentences for effect.
I used some proper nouns to make my description sound more real.	I chose proper nouns to name different elements in the history of my dystopian world.	I created and named characters and periods in the history of my dystopian world with carefully chosen proper nouns.
I expanded some noun phrases with adjectives or non-finite or relative clauses.	I expanded some noun phrases in different ways to give the reader more detail about the history of my dystopian world.	I expanded some noun phrases in a range of ways to give the reader detailed information and influence their response to the history of my dystopian world.

67

5 Constructing a point of view

Learning objective

- Understand how choice of pronouns, nouns and verbs can influence the reader's response to characters and their points of view

The narrative viewpoint of a text is the viewpoint from which the story is told. *The Hunger Games* is narrated in the **first person** by its hero, Katniss Everdeen. However, the writer skilfully uses Everdeen's narration to reveal other characters' thoughts and feelings (their point of view).

Activity 1

Look again at the extract from *The Hunger Games* in which Katniss tells the reader about the mayor's speech on the day of the Reaping.

1 Pick out two sentences which hint at the mayor's thoughts and feelings (his point of view) about the history of Panem.

   a In what tone of voice might the mayor express these thoughts and feelings?

   b Write two or three sentences explaining your choices about his point of view and tone.

2 Pick out two sentences which hint at Katniss's thoughts and feelings (her point of view) about the history of Panem.

   a In what tone of voice might Katniss express these thoughts and feelings?

   b Write two or three sentences explaining your choices about her point of view and tone.

Just as the clock strikes two, the mayor steps up to the podium and begins to read. It's the same story every year. He tells of the history of Panem, the country that rose up out of the ashes of a place that was once called North America. He lists the disasters, the droughts, the storms, the fires, the encroaching seas that swallowed up so much of the land, the brutal war for what little sustenance remained. The result was Panem, a shining Capitol ringed by thirteen districts, which brought peace and prosperity to its citizens. Then came the Dark Days, the uprising of the districts against the Capitol. Twelve were defeated, the thirteenth obliterated. The Treaty of Treason gave us new laws to guarantee peace and, as our yearly reminder that the Dark Days must never be repeated, it gave us the Hunger Games.

The rules of the Hunger Games are simple. In punishment for the uprising, each of the twelve districts must provide one girl and one boy, called tributes, to participate. The twenty-four tributes will be imprisoned in a vast outdoor arena that could hold anything from a burning desert to a frozen wasteland. Over a period of several weeks, the competitors must fight to the death. The last tribute standing wins.

WRITER'S WORKSHOP: Giving different points of view

In the extract, the narrator reports the mayor's speech to the reader. The writer uses this reported speech to suggest to the reader that the narrator and the mayor have two very different points of view.

How can I use pronouns and related determiners to present two points of view?

The start of the extract appears to be written in the **third person**. The narrator does not refer to herself at all:

> (He) tells of the history of Panem

> (He) lists the disasters

third-person pronoun

It is only at the end of the first paragraph that we are reminded that the mayor's words are being reported to us by the narrator:

> The Treaty of Treason gave (us) new laws to guarantee peace and, as (our) yearly reminder that the Dark Days must never be repeated, it gave (us) the Hunger Games.

The (first-person plural pronouns) and the (first-person plural determiner) reveal that the story is being told by a first-person narrator. This reminds us that Katniss's point of view is different from the mayor's.

How can I use abstract nouns to reveal a character's point of view?

Compare the mayor's point of view with that of Katniss, the narrator.

The mayor describes the ruling city of Panem as:

> a shining Capitol ringed by thirteen districts, which brought (peace) and (prosperity) to its citizens

The mayor uses positive (abstract nouns) to describe the benefits which the rules of Panem have given the people.

Katniss tells us about a violent game played to the death, known as

> the (Hunger) Games.

This (abstract noun) and Katniss's explanation of the Games suggest that not every citizen enjoys the peace and prosperity which the mayor boasts about!

Concrete nouns are the words we use to identify physical objects, people and places. Abstract nouns identify ideas, feelings and emotions which you cannot see, hear, smell, touch or taste, e.g. happiness, courage, misery.

69

How can I use verbs to reveal a character's point of view?

Immediately after talking of the peace which the Capitol has brought to Panem, the mayor describes how the Capitol reacted to the uprising, or rebellion, of the thirteen districts:

Twelve were (defeated,) the thirteenth (obliterated.)

verb

What do these two verbs suggest about the Capitol's and the mayor's attitude to uprisings and rebellion?

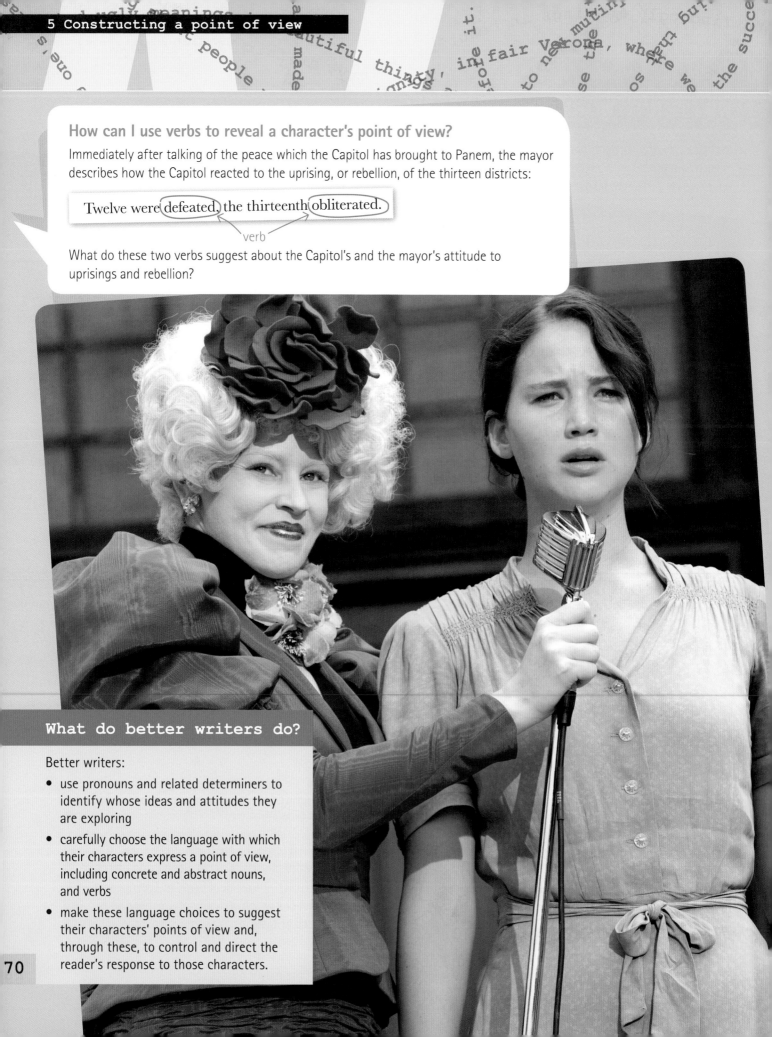

What do better writers do?

Better writers:

- use pronouns and related determiners to identify whose ideas and attitudes they are exploring
- carefully choose the language with which their characters express a point of view, including concrete and abstract nouns, and verbs
- make these language choices to suggest their characters' points of view and, through these, to control and direct the reader's response to those characters.

Activity 2

1 What do you think of the mayor and his point of view? Support your answer by referring to the text.

2 What do you think of Katniss and her point of view? Support your answer by referring to the text.

3 Look again at the paragraph you wrote about the history of your imagined dystopian world in Lesson 4, Activity 2 on page 67.

   a Identify three words or phrases that reveal one of your characters' point of view.

   b How could you identify and develop one or more of your characters' points of view? Add a second paragraph to your history, in which you experiment with your choice of:

   - pronouns and related determiners – how will your narrator tell the reader about another character's point of view?
   - abstract nouns – what have the rulers of your world promised its people? What does the narrator of your story experience or hope for?
   - verbs – how could your choice of verbs reveal the ways in which the rulers of your world have treated its people?

CHECK YOUR WRITING

Look at your writing from Activity 2, question 3b and annotate your writing to show where you have included:
   - pronouns and related determiners to present two points of view
   - abstract nouns and verbs to reveal a character's point of view.

Look at the table below, decide which column best describes the paragraph you wrote in this lesson.

I deliberately chose abstract nouns and verbs to create the impression I wanted my reader to have of the characters.	I carefully and deliberately chose a varied range of abstract nouns and verbs to create the impression I wanted my reader to have of the characters.	I imagined and created a dystopian future, its values and its characters, consistently aiming to influence the reader's response to them with my language choice throughout.
I chose my narrative viewpoint, thinking carefully about how the reader would respond to the narrator.	I chose my narrative viewpoint thinking carefully about how the reader would respond to the narrator and to other characters' points of view. I used appropriate pronouns and related determiners.	I chose my narrative viewpoint so that I could show and contrast two characters' conflicting points of view and emphasise their differences, using appropriate pronouns and related determiners.

6 Dystopia and today's society

Learning objective

- Understand how writers explore current issues through fictional dystopian societies

Dystopian writers often take a concern from today's society and imagine it taken to an extreme in a future world.

In *The Hunger Games*, the author takes the format of some television talent programmes and re-imagines them in a future of gladiatorial battles.

Activity 1

Read the opening of the science-fiction story *Harrison Bergeron* below.

The year was 2081 and everybody was finally equal. They weren't only equal before God and the law. They were equal every which way. Nobody was smarter than anybody else. Nobody was better looking than anybody else. Nobody was stronger or quicker than anybody else. All this equality was due to the 211th, 212th, and 213th Amendments to the Constitution, and to the unceasing vigilance of agents of the United States Handicapper General.

1   Which current concern has the writer chosen to take to an extreme? Choose one word that summarises the main principle of the society in the extract.

2   The writer describes how everyone in this future is equally smart, equally strong and equally quick. How might the United States government of 2081 and the Handicapper General have achieved this situation? Try to think of two or three different ways.

3   Do you think the world described in the story opening above sounds like a utopia or a dystopia? Write two or three sentences explaining your answer.

Activity 2

Now read the next part of the story below.

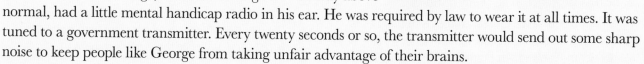

Some things about living still weren't quite right, though. April, for instance, still drove people crazy by not being springtime. And it was in that clammy month that the H-G men took George and Hazel Bergeron's fourteen-year-old son, Harrison, away.

It was tragic, all right, but George and Hazel couldn't think about it very hard. Hazel had a perfectly average intelligence, which meant she couldn't think about anything except in short bursts. And George, while his intelligence was way above normal, had a little mental handicap radio in his ear. He was required by law to wear it at all times. It was tuned to a government transmitter. Every twenty seconds or so, the transmitter would send out some sharp noise to keep people like George from taking unfair advantage of their brains.

George and Hazel were watching television. There were tears on Hazel's cheeks, but she'd forgotten for the moment what they were about.

On the television screen were ballerinas. A buzzer sounded in George's head. His thoughts fled in panic, like bandits from a burglar alarm.

'That was a real pretty dance, that dance they just did,' said Hazel.

'Huh,' said George.

'That dance – it was nice,' said Hazel.

'Yup,' said George. He tried to think a little about the ballerinas. They weren't really very good – no better than anybody else would have been, anyway. They were burdened with sash weights and bags of birdshot, and their faces were masked, so that no one, seeing a free and graceful gesture or a pretty face, would feel like something the cat drug in. George was toying with the vague notion that maybe dancers shouldn't be handicapped. But he didn't get very far with it before another noise in his ear radio scattered his thoughts.

1 a Why does George have to wear an earpiece?

   b Why does Hazel not have to wear an earpiece?

   c The writer describes Hazel's 'perfectly average intelligence, which meant she couldn't think about anything except in short bursts.' What do you think the writer is implying about:

   • Hazel?   • equality in the world of 2081?

2 a What impression does the extract give you of the US government and the Handicapper General? Support your answer with two or three quotations from the extract.

   b Does this story have anything in common with the other fiction you have explored in this unit?

3 On the next few pages, you are going to complete a longer piece of writing. Think about all the different dystopian worlds you have explored in this unit so far. What are the key elements of the genre which you would include in your own dystopian short story?

4 The story you will be writing on the next few pages will be set in a school.

   a What concerns do you have about school and education? Think of at least three.

   b How could you take one of these concerns to an extreme to create a dystopian short story about schools in the near or distant future? Write a short paragraph, like the extract from Activity 1, that establishes the dystopian school setting.

Assessment: Dystopian openings

Learning objective

- Understand how to write a story opening using features of the dystopian genre

So far in this unit, you have explored some of the key elements of dystopian fiction, including:

- a setting that might at first appear utopian but where the writer soon hints that something is not quite right. An example is the island in *Lord of the Flies*.
- a shocking change to society and how it can have frightening, unforeseen consequences. An example is the disappearance of all adults in *Gone*.
- a fictional world based on real concerns in the author's own society that can spin out of control if they're not resolved. An example is *The Hunger Games*, in connection with competition in current reality television.
- a fictional society where values have been taken to an extreme. An example is the concept of equality in *Harrison Bergeron*.

You have seen how better writers make choices, such as:

- using nouns and short and expanded noun phrases to give an impression of a setting
- using adverbs and adverbial phrases along with sentence structure to create a sense of sudden change or drama
- choosing nouns, proper nouns and a range of expanded noun phrases to create a history for your dystopian society and influence the reader's response to it
- using pronoun, noun and verb choice to convey different characters' points of view.

In this task, you will need to use all the skills and understanding you have developed so far to write the opening two or three paragraphs of a dystopian story about a school of the future.

PLAN

Follow the steps below and opposite to collect your ideas and think about the decisions you must make before you start writing.

1   **What values will my school have?**

Read the text below. It is taken from a real school prospectus.

A specialist sports academy

Teamwork, commitment, determination and confidence – these are the qualities we encourage in all our students.

We are a specialist sports academy that embeds physical activity into every school day. We believe that sport can be used to enhance learning as well as improve health and engender a sense of achievement. It encourages students to become happy, healthy and well-balanced individuals.

With our students repeatedly performing above the national average in all subjects, the sports specialism ensures students strive for excellence across the whole curriculum, making them attractive to universities, colleges and employers alike.

Look at the prospectus. What are the principles of the education at this school? Build a word bank of nouns from the same **lexical field** that suggest the school's sporting values.

> determination, fitness equipment, winning

2 **What aspects of the dystopian genre will I use?**

In Lesson 6, Activity 2, you thought about school and education and how you could use your concerns to write a dystopian story.

Think again about ways in which a school's ideals could be distorted into an extreme, dystopic vision, and imagine some extreme ideals and rules for your school.

If, for example, you wanted to write about a school in which sport and fitness have been taken to an extreme, your ideas might look something like the spider diagram on the right.

3 **What narrative viewpoint will I use?**

- Should you choose to tell your story using third-person or first-person narrative?

- If you choose a first-person narrator, which character will it be?

> A teacher? The headteacher?
>
> A newcomer to the school? A student?
>
> Or someone else?
>
> Someone who supports or enforces the school's ideals?
>
> Or someone who questions and wants to change them?

> A **lexical field** is a word group; for example, 'palm tree', 'sun' and 'coconut' belong to the same lexical field of a desert island utopia.

Students have to eat ten portions of fruit and vegetables each day before starting work.

All tasks, including written work, can only be completed in groups because community spirit is key and 'there is no "I" in team'!

Sweat production is measured for each student. If they don't produce enough each day they must make up the difference by lifting weights.

Anyone who gives up or shows lack of determination and commitment is put on the fitness bikes to generate green energy and increase their pride in the school before they can use any more electricity.

4 What will I write about in my opening paragraphs?

Your opening could:

a explain the rules and ideals of this dystopian school to the reader. Some ideas to help you do this are below. You could...

... open your story with the headteacher's speech, a little like the mayor's speech in *The Hunger Games*

... have a student explaining to a newcomer how the system works

... use the characters' actions and dialogue to show the reader how it works, as in *Harrison Bergeron*.

b describe the setting of your story. Some ideas to help you are below. You could...

... use your setting to help show what kind of school it is

... suggest a utopia but one which the reader soon suspects is not quite as perfect as it seems

... describe the events which led the school to change its ideals and rules.

WRITE

You are now ready to write your extract.

Your task

Write the opening of a dystopian short story about a school of the future. Aim to write between 150 and 200 words.

REFLECT

When you have completed your opening, read it through carefully.

- Are you pleased with it?
- Which of the statements on the checklist do you feel you have achieved and which could you improve?

☐ I think I have used some key features of the dystopian genre in my opening

☐ I think I have chosen the most effective narrative viewpoint for my opening

☐ I think I have successfully imagined and clearly shown the ideals and rules of the school

☐ I think I have effectively described the setting of my story

☐ I think I have clearly shown the history of the school and influenced the reader's response to it

☐ I think I have shown different characters' points of view

☐ I think I have created a sense of drama

1   For each of the statements you feel you have achieved, write a sentence explaining the effect and impact of your choices, for example:

> *I think I have shown the history of the school and influenced the reader's*
> *response to it by inventing some proper nouns to name past events in the*
> *school's history and chosen dramatic abstract nouns like 'chaos' and 'hatred'*
> *to describe their consequences.*

2   Choose one or two areas in your writing which you feel you could improve.

   a   Working on your own, or with a partner, look back at the relevant pages in this unit to remind yourself of the choices you would make and techniques you would use to improve your writing in those one or two areas.

   b   Write a sentence or two explaining how you will improve your writing in those one or two areas.

   c   Make the improvements to your writing.

CHECK YOUR WRITING

⬇   Looking at the table below, decide which column you think best describes the writing you crafted in this assessment.

I chose my narrative viewpoint thinking carefully about how the reader would respond to the narrator.	I chose my narrative viewpoint thinking carefully about how the reader would respond to the narrator and to other characters' points of view.	I chose my narrative viewpoint so that I could show and contrast two characters' conflicting points of view and emphasise their differences.
I deliberately chose some verbs, nouns and noun phrases to create the impression I wanted my reader to have of the characters and setting.	I carefully and deliberately chose a varied range of nouns, verbs and crafted nouns and noun phrases to create the impression I wanted my reader to have of the characters and setting.	I imagined and created a dystopian future, its values and its characters, consistently aiming to influence the reader's response to them with my language choice throughout.
I planned and wrote my opening, deliberately choosing and developing key features of the dystopia genre. I thought about how it would grab and hold the reader's interest.	I planned and wrote my opening, deliberately choosing and adapting key features of the dystopia genre. I thought carefully about the effect that the characters, setting and language would have on the reader.	I planned and wrote my opening, thinking about the ideas I wanted to explore and how I could present them in order to influence the reader's response.

7 Selling an idea

Learning objectives

- Understand how writers of dystopian fiction include elements of the familiar within a disturbing world in order to unsettle the reader

- Understand how language can be crafted to persuade and control the reader in dystopian fiction

Authors of dystopian fiction sometimes use familiar ideas and language to help us believe in the world they have created. However, there are often subtle, strange differences they include in order to make us feel disconcerted and to make us think about an issue.

Activity 1

1 Read the extract opposite from the novel *Do Androids Dream of Electric Sheep?* by Philip K. Dick. It describes how the state is trying to persuade the American people to move to its colony on Mars, as they lose control of the deteriorating state on Earth.

   a What questions does the title of this novel raise? What questions might the author be trying to raise in the reader's mind?

   b What seems familiar to you about the setting and language in this extract?

   c What seems unfamiliar about the setting and language in this extract?

2 The writer has included a strange and unfamiliar concept, but in a familiar setting. Can you identify any contemporary concerns that the writer might be exploring in this novel?

The TV set shouted, ' — duplicates the **halcyon** days of the **pre-Civil War Southern states**! Either as body servants or tireless field hands, the custom-tailored humanoid robot designed specifically for YOUR UNIQUE NEEDS, FOR YOU AND YOU ALONE — given to you on your arrival absolutely free, equipped fully, as specified by you before your departure from Earth; this loyal, trouble-free companion in the greatest, boldest adventure contrived by man in modern history will provide —' It continued on and on.

I wonder if I'm late for work, Isidore wondered as he scraped. He did not own a working clock; generally he depended on the TV for time signals, but today was Interspace Horizons Day, evidently. Anyhow the TV claimed this to be the fifth (or sixth?) anniversary of the founding of New America, the chief U.S. settlement on Mars. And his TV set, being partly broken, picked up only the channel which had been nationalized during the war and still remained so; the government in Washington, with its **colonization** program, constituted the sole **sponsor** which Isidore found himself forced to listen to. 'Let's hear from Mrs. Maggie Klugman,' the TV announcer suggested to John Isidore, who wanted only to know the time. 'A recent immigrant to Mars, Mrs. Klugman in an interview taped live in New New York had this to say. Mrs. Klugman, how would you contrast your life back on contaminated Earth with your new life here in a world rich with every imaginable possibility?' A pause, and then a tired, dry, middle-aged, female voice said, 'I think what I and my family of three noticed most was the dignity.' 'The dignity, Mrs. Klugman?' the announcer asked. 'Yes,' Mrs. Klugman, now of New New York, Mars, said. 'It's a hard thing to explain. Having a servant you can depend on in these troubled times . . . I find it reassuring.'

'Back on Earth, Mrs. Klugman, in the old days, did you also worry about finding yourself classified, ahem, as a special?'

'Oh, my husband and myself worried ourselves nearly to death. Of course, once we **emigrated** that worry vanished, fortunately forever.'

Do Androids Dream of Electric Sheep?

The novel which became BLADE RUNNER

Glossary

colonization: settling and establishing control over an area

sponsor: a group or person that offers financial backing for a project or undertaking

emigrate: to leave a country or region to settle in another

halcyon: prosperous, golden

pre-Civil War Southern states: the South of the U.S. at a time of change in America from a farming to an urbanised powerful economy. The southern states gave more support at this time to the tradition of slavery in America, while the northern states largely supported the right to freedom of black slaves.

WRITER'S WORKSHOP: The language of power and persuasion

The advert in the novel extract on page 79 uses language we recognise from our own screens, but is employing it to advertise humanoid robots to use in alternative worlds. Writers of dystopian fiction often need to use persuasive language to sell their new ideas to the reader and sometimes to show how their fictional characters who hold power persuade and control others, too.

How can I use adjectives to make objects or ideas sound appealing?

You can use noun phrases in which the noun is pre-modified with a series of emotive adjectives to persuade people of the value of a product, service or idea. For example:

A **delicious**, **rich** and **creamy** dessert…

adjective

Humanoids are a **stylish**, **contemporary** and **practical** addition to your home.

adjective

Look again at the advert in the extract on page 79. Can you find any examples of stacked adjectives pre-modifying or post-modifying a noun which make the robot sound appealing?

How can I use sentence structure to give as much positive information and description as possible?

Advertisers often use non-finite clauses to give further information about their products. You can do the same to give your reader more information about an item or idea in your dystopian world.

A non-finite clause is headed with a non-finite verb; for example a past participle such as:

designed   made   provided   covered

Non-finite clauses can be used to post-modify a noun:

efficient robots, programmed to obey and designed to last for decades.

███ noun

███ non-finite clause post-modifying the noun

░░░ comma separates the non-finite clause and the noun

Can you find any examples of non-finite clauses in the extract advert? Do these examples of persuasive language make you want to buy a humanoid for yourself?

What do better writers do?

Better writers:

- influence their readers using a range of persuasive language
- use persuasive language to show how people have control over others
- stack adjectives in expanded noun phrases to emphasise the positive qualities of a product or service
- post-modify nouns with non-finite clauses which add detailed, descriptive information.

Activity 2

1 Imagine a robot animal or humanoid which might be available for sale in the world of *Do Androids Dream of Electric Sheep?* or your own dystopian world. You could, for example, imagine an electric hamster, an electric humanoid mother, or an electric humanoid lunch supervisor.

2 Write a short advert for your robot in the style of the one from the extract on page 79. You could use some of these language features:

- stacked adjectives to highlight positive features of your product
- non-finite clauses to add detail about the product.

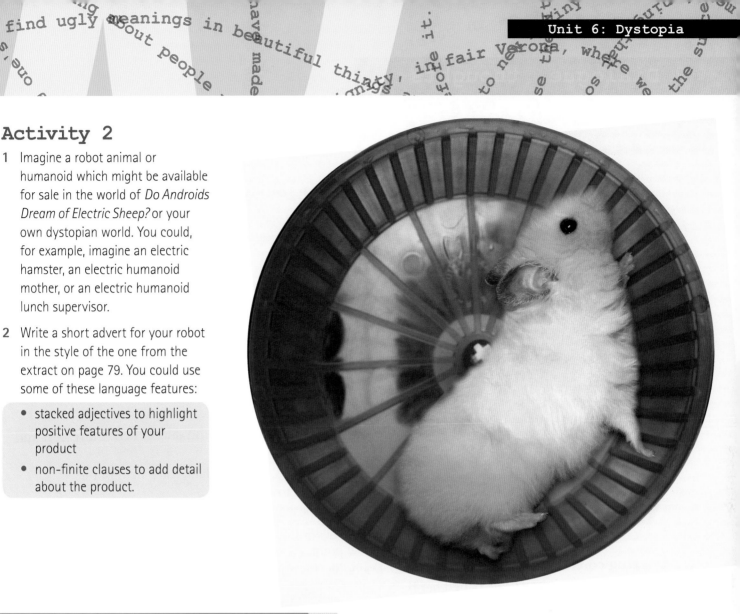

CHECK YOUR WRITING

➡ Read your advert aloud, as if it were a TV advert.

- Which of your writing choices are you most pleased with?

- How could you change some of your choices to make your advert even more persuasive? Make some notes on your advert, highlighting what is good and what could be improved. It might look something like this:

> Choose from a wonderful range of fun, furry, realistic hamsters now. These hamsters have a range of brilliant features and are the best on the market.

▢ Good use of imperative verb to persuade the reader.

▢ Good choice of stacked adjectives and alliteration. It sounds really positive.

▢ This sentence is ok but perhaps you could have added some persuasive detail about the different features.

➡ Use your notes to make your advert even more persuasive.

81

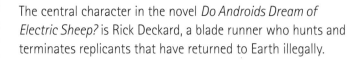

8 Dialogue, thoughts and feelings

Learning objective

- Understand how writers use dialogue to convey characters' thoughts and feelings

The central character in the novel *Do Androids Dream of Electric Sheep?* is Rick Deckard, a blade runner who hunts and terminates replicants that have returned to Earth illegally.

Activity 1

Read the opening paragraphs of the novel *Do Androids Dream of Electric Sheep?* below.

A merry little surge of electricity piped by automatic alarm from the **mood organ** beside his bed awakened Rick Deckard. Surprised – it always surprised him to find himself awake without prior notice – he rose from the bed, stood up in his multicolored pajamas, and stretched. Now, in her bed, his wife Iran opened her gray, unmerry eyes, blinked, then groaned and shut her eyes again.

'You set your **Penfield** too weak,' he said to her. 'I'll reset it and you'll be awake and – '

'Keep your hand off my settings.' Her voice held bitter sharpness. 'I don't *want* to be awake.'

He seated himself beside her, bent over her, and explained softly, 'If you set the surge up high enough, you'll be glad you're awake; that's the whole point. At setting *C* it overcomes the **threshold barring consciousness**, as it does for me.' Friendlily, because he felt well-disposed toward the world – *his* setting had been at *D* – he patted her bare, pale shoulder.

'Get your crude cop's hand away,' Iran said.

'I'm not a cop – ' He felt irritable, now, although he hadn't dialed for it.

'You're worse,' his wife said, her eyes still shut. 'You're a murderer hired by the cops.'

'I've never killed a human being in my life.' His irritability had risen, now; had become outright hostility.

Iran said, 'Just those poor **andys**.'

'I notice you've never had any hesitation as to spending the bounty money I bring home on whatever momentarily attracts your attention.' He rose, strode to the console of his mood organ. 'Instead of saving,' he said, 'so we could buy a real sheep, to replace that fake electric one upstairs. A mere electric animal, and me earning all that I've worked my way up to through the years.'

At his console he hesitated between dialing for a thalamic suppressant (which would abolish his mood of rage) or a thalamic stimulant (which would make him irked enough to win the argument).

'If you dial,' Iran said, eyes open and watching, 'for greater venom, then I'll dial the same. I'll dial the maximum and you'll see a fight that makes every argument we've had up to now seem like nothing. Dial and see; just try me.' She rose swiftly, loped to the console of her own mood organ, stood glaring at him, waiting.

Glossary

andys: slang for androids – replicant humanoid robot

mood organ: a device, imagined by the writer, which allows the user to choose and control the emotions they feel

Penfield: a brand of mood organ

threshold barring consciousness: at setting C, the mood organ wakes the user up in a good mood

1 What do you learn from the extract about:

 a Rick Deckard

 b Iran Deckard

 c their relationship

 d the world in which the novel is set?

2 Support each of your answers to question 1 with a quotation from the extract and a sentence or two explaining how or why the quotation suggests this.

WRITER'S WORKSHOP: Using dialogue to convey characters' moods

How can I use reporting verbs to show the manner in which speech is expressed?

Dialogue can be a powerful tool to help a writer to convey the mood of their characters in a dystopian world.

> identifier: indicates who is speaking; for example, 'he' or 'Rick'.

1 **Reporting verbs**, such as 'to say' and 'to tell', are used to show the speaker in dialogue. But reporting verbs can also be used to show the way in which things are said. For example:

| shouted | whispered | screamed |

2 You can also add adverbs and adverbial phrases to modify the reporting verb, adding information about *how* dialogue is spoken. For example, look at this phrase:

He explained softly   ■ reporting verb   ■ adverb   ■ identifier

3 Sometimes, though, writers choose the simplest reporting verbs and do not modify them. For example:

Iran said, 'Just those poor andys.'

The writer has not modified this reporting verb. Why do you think the writer made this decision?

4 Sometimes writers use no identifier or reporting verb at all but leave the reader to infer who is speaking, for example:

'You set your Penfield too weak,' he said to her. 'I'll reset it and you'll be awake and –'
'Keep your hand off my settings.' Her voice held bitter sharpness.

There is no identifier or reporting verb here. The reader has to infer it is Iran speaking.

This reporting verb is not modified with an adverb.

Why do you think the writer added a description of Iran's voice in a separate sentence, instead of using an identifier along with a reporting verb and an adverb? Try rewriting the sentences above, adding reporting verbs and modifying them with adverbs. What different effects can you create?

83

What do better writers do?

Better writers:

- make choices in dialogue that tell the reader about the characters, their relationships or their world

- choose from a range of reporting verbs to suggest the tone in which dialogue is spoken

- use adverbs or adverbial phrases to modify reporting verbs

- sometimes use the simplest, most common reporting verbs, or no reporting verb at all to focus the reader on the dialogue itself.

Activity 2

1 Write a short piece of dialogue between two characters in a dystopian story, experimenting with some of the choices you learnt about on page 83.

Activity 3

Now you are going to write your own film script based on the dialogue from the passage from *Do Androids Dream of Electric Sheep?*

1 Look at the example on the opposite page to familiarise yourself with the conventions of scriptwriting.

2 Using the dialogue from the extract from *Do Androids Dream of Electric Sheep?* on page 82, write your own short film script reflecting this episode.

3 Consider the decisions a scriptwriter must make as you decide what to select, add and delete from the original prose.

> How can I convey the significant setting in a few words of narrative description?

> How can I convey the fact that Rick is wondering whether to use a thalamic stimulant or suppressant? Through pauses? Through slow movements?

> How can I convey Iran's thoughts, feelings and attitudes?

1. EXT. DAY – NEW YORK CITY.

A Rolls Royce drives down 42nd Street.

CUT TO: INT. CAR

A very English gentleman figure sits in the rear seat, sipping champagne. This is CHARLES DE VERNAY. Elegant, dressed in the finest Saville Row suit. He has his laptop next to him on the seat and idly taps the keyboard. His driver, JONES, pays close attentions to the road ahead, whilst also looking in the rear view mirror every now and again to make sure all is peaceful and calm in the back.

JONES   We should be arriving in a few moments, Sir.

Charles looks up and peers through the window.

CHARLES   (quietly) Thank you, Jones.

Charles puts down his champagne and pays more attention to his laptop screen.

2. CUT TO: INT. HELICOPTER - NEW YORK SKYLINE

A helicopter flying over New York. The PILOT's face is masked by a black visor. Next to him sits a WOMAN who is concentrating on the screen of her laptop.

WOMAN   Can you pick him up on your tracker?

PILOT   He's going along 42nd, Ma'am. Do you want me to go down a little and see if we can spot him?

WOMAN   As close as you can.

PILOT   As close as we're allowed.

3. CUT TO: EXT. DAY – NEW YORK SKYLINE.

Shot of helicopter flying over New York skyline. We can see the Empire State building in the background.

PILOT   He should be right below us now.

Annotations:
- 'Slug line' at start of scene shows where and when the action is taking place
- Use of present tense
- Stage directions show what characters should do
- Characters' names in capitals
- Guidance as to how dialogue should be spoken
- Indicates scene number

CHECK YOUR WRITING

➡ Once you have written your script, read it aloud with a partner and answer the following questions.
- Have you managed to convey the relationship between the characters effectively in the fewest words possible?
- Are there any places where you can reduce the number of words you have used?

➡ Look at your script again. Try to cut your text down by 15 words without losing any crucial elements of the relationships or action.

9 The language of power

Learning objective

- Understand how language can be used to manipulate people

In many of the dystopian societies you have looked at, powerful leaders wield huge control over their people. Language choice is one of the key ways in which rulers of dystopian worlds dominate and manipulate ordinary people.

Activity 1

1 George Orwell was a novelist and writer of essays. Read the quote on the right from one of his most famous essays.

2 What do you think Orwell means?

3 Look back at the extract from *The Hunger Games* on page 64. In what ways is the mayor of Panem's speech an example of Orwell's comments on political language?

> Political language – and with variations this is true of all political parties, from Conservatives to Anarchists – is designed to make lies sound truthful and murder respectable, and to give an appearance of solidity to pure wind.

Activity 2

In recent years, the growing power of television and social media such as Twitter has given more importance to short 'soundbites' rather than long political speeches. Politicians know this. When writing their speeches, they try to include snappy phrases that can be easily picked up and promoted by the media.

1 Read these famous political soundbites.

> Pennies don't fall from heaven – they have to be earned here on earth. (Margaret Thatcher, 1979)

> If you want something said, ask a man. If you want something done, ask a woman. (Margaret Thatcher, 1965)

> You're an analogue politician in a digital age. (David Cameron talking about Gordon Brown, 2006)

> Change will not come if we wait for some other person or some other time. We are the ones we've been waiting for. We are the change that we seek. (Barack Obama, 2008)

2 How have the politicians' speechwriters made them memorable?

Activity 3

George Orwell's novel *Animal Farm* tells the story of a farm where the animals overthrow the farmer. They take control and create their own rules to organise their new utopian society. Read the extract on the right.

1   Why do you think these are called 'The Seven Commandments'?

2   What do these commandments suggest about the animals' attitude to their former leader, the farmer?

THE SEVEN COMMANDMENTS

Whatever goes upon two legs is an enemy.

Whatever goes upon four legs, or has wings, is a friend.

No animal shall wear clothes.

No animal shall sleep in a bed.

No animal shall drink alcohol.

No animal shall kill any other animal.

All animals are equal.

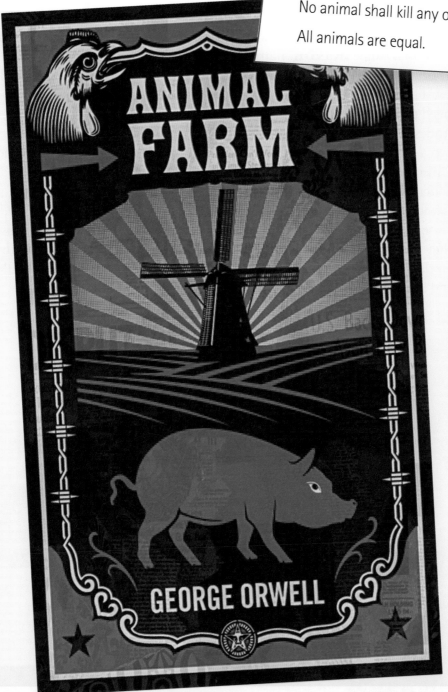

3 The commandments are written by the pigs, as they are the cleverest animals on the farm. Read the extract below, in which Snowball, one of the cleverest pigs, tries to explain the commandments to the less intelligent creatures.

4 The pigs use a lot of language designed to control the other animals and influence their thoughts and opinions ('Snowball proved to them that this was not so'). Think about what Orwell is suggesting.

   a Why do the birds accept what they cannot understand? Look at the noun phrase 'organ of propulsion' and the abstract noun 'mischief'.

   b Why do the pigs write the simplified commandment 'Four legs good, two legs bad' in larger letters at the end of the barn?

   c Why do the sheep constantly chant the simplified commandment?

The stupider animals, such as the sheep, hens, and ducks, were unable to learn the Seven Commandments by heart. After much thought Snowball declared that the Seven Commandments could in effect be reduced to a single **maxim**, namely: 'Four legs good, two legs bad.' This, he said, contained the essential principle of **Animalism**. Whoever had thoroughly grasped it would be safe from human influences. The birds at first objected, since it seemed to them that they also had two legs, but Snowball proved to them that this was not so.

   'A bird's wing, comrades,' he said, 'is an organ of propulsion and not of manipulation. It should therefore be regarded as a leg. The distinguishing mark of man is the HAND, the instrument with which he does all his mischief.'

   The birds did not understand Snowball's long words, but they accepted his explanation, and all the humbler animals set to work to learn the new maxim by heart. FOUR LEGS GOOD, TWO LEGS BAD, was inscribed on the end wall of the barn, above the Seven Commandments and in bigger letters. When they had once got it by heart, the sheep developed a great liking for this maxim, and often as they lay in the field they would all start bleating 'Four legs good, two legs bad! Four legs good, two legs bad!' and keep it up for hours on end, never growing tired of it.

Glossary

maxim: a rule or principle
Animalism: the political philosophy by which the animals run their own farm

Activity 4

1 Imagine you live in a society which encourages its people to strive for physical perfection and beauty.

   a Write a list of commandments that outline the values of this society.

   b Can you summarise your commandments in one short, simplified commandment that everyone will be able to remember and understand?

2 Your leader has asked you to write a text explaining this society's values to its people. Write this text, which could be in one of the following formats:

   • a TV advert
   • the opening to a speech
   • the text for a billboard or poster
   • something else.

In your text you will need to explain:

   • **how** people should follow your commandments
   • **why** they should follow your commandments.

To do this you will need to use language that will control and influence people's thoughts and actions. Think about the noun phrases you use, choosing appropriate determiners, nouns, proper nouns and adjectives. Consider:

   • the structure of your text – will you repeat words, phrases or sentences?
   • the types of sentence you use – short, simple sentences or longer complex sentences with relative clauses or non-finite clauses?
   • how you will make your text persuasive, perhaps by using imperatives or including familiar language for the reader or listener.

3 Look carefully at what you have written. Are there any sentences that you could edit into memorable soundbites in order to influence and control?

89

10 Science and power

Learning objectives

- Understand how proper nouns can be chosen to convey a structured society in an imaginary world

- Understand how short, simple sentences can emphasise key moments in a narrative that highlight the dystopian features of a plot

Glossary

eugenics: a movement which argues that human beings should take control of their evolution by preventing people considered to have less desirable and valuable qualities from reproducing. Enforced sterilisation was legalised in some of the United States of America between 1909 and 1981. In that time, approximately 60,000 people were sterilised. The majority were criminals, mentally ill or simply poor

Some writers have been inspired to write dystopian fiction by the power of science and their concerns about its impact on society.

Activity 1

Aldous Huxley wrote *Brave New World* in 1931, when a number of people argued that **eugenics** could improve the human race. In the novel, Huxley imagines the world in the twenty-sixth century, when humans are not born but are created in laboratories in one of five genetically-engineered classes.

In *Brave New World*, the Director of Hatcheries and Conditioning is responsible for the creation and education of all humans in the twenty-sixth century.

Read the extract below, in which the Director of Hatcheries and Conditioning is inspecting the laboratories where this conditioning takes place.

Fifty yards of tiptoeing brought them to a door which the Director cautiously opened. They stepped over the threshold into the twilight of a shuttered dormitory. Eighty cots stood in a row against the wall. There was a sound of light regular breathing and a continuous murmur, as of very faint voices remotely whispering.

A nurse rose as they entered and came to attention before the Director.

'What's the lesson this afternoon?' he asked.

'[...]**Elementary Class Consciousness**.'

The Director walked slowly down the long line of cots. Rosy and relaxed with sleep, eighty little boys and girls lay softly breathing. There was a whisper under every pillow. The D.H.C. halted and, bending over one of the little beds, listened attentively.

'Elementary Class Consciousness, did you say? Let's have it repeated a little louder by the **trumpet**.'

At the end of the room a loud speaker projected from the wall. The Director walked up to it and pressed a switch.

'... all wear green,' said a soft but very distinct voice, beginning in the middle of a sentence, 'and Delta children wear khaki. Oh no, I don't want to play with Delta children. And Epsilons are still worse. They're too stupid to be able to read or write. Besides they wear black, which is such a beastly colour. I'm so glad I'm a Beta.'

There was a pause; then the voice began again. 'Alpha children wear grey. They work much harder than we do, because they're so frightfully clever. I'm really awfully glad I'm a Beta, because I don't work so hard. And then we are much better than the Gammas and Deltas. Gammas are stupid. They all wear green, and Delta children wear khaki. Oh no, I don't want to play with Delta children. And Epsilons are still worse. They're too stupid to be able ...'

The Director pushed back the switch. The voice was silent. Only its thin ghost continued to mutter from beneath the eighty pillows. 'They'll have that repeated forty or fifty times more before they wake; then again on Thursday, and again on Saturday. A hundred and twenty times, three times a week for thirty months. After which they go on to a more advanced lesson. [...] Till at last the child's mind is these suggestions, and the sum of the suggestions is the child's mind. And not the child's mind only. The adult's mind too – all his life long.'

Glossary

Elementary Class Consciousness: basic learning to create an awareness of the different classes in society
trumpet: loudspeaker

1 a What are the names given to the five different classes of human beings created in these laboratories? Write them down in rank order, from the most to the least valuable.

   b What other information can you gather about these five different classes?

2 What do you think is the purpose of teaching the children this class structure?

3 a What is the main method of teaching used in the laboratory?

   b Where, in other dystopias you have explored, has this method of influencing people played a part?

   c Do external messages in the real world influence the way that *you* think and make decisions?

WRITER'S WORKSHOP: Creating a dystopian context

How can I use proper nouns to create an imaginary future?

On page 64 (Lesson 4), you looked at an extract from *The Hunger Games* and explored how Panem controls its people's attitudes to the past through the names it gives to events in its history:

The Treaty of Treason   the Dark Days

In *Brave New World*, it is not just people's attitude to the past which is controlled by language. It is their attitude to themselves and to each other. Huxley conveys this by imagining the human race divided into five groups, and by naming each one with a proper noun, from the Alphas to the Epsilons.

Why do you think Huxley chose these names for the five classes of people?

How can I use short sentences to highlight a key moment in a narrative?

A simple sentence consists of one clause and contains one main verb.

In Lesson 2, you looked at how sentence length controls the pace of action in a narrative.

In the extract from *Brave New World* on pages 90 and 91, the writer has used simple sentences to emphasise key movements in the narrative that highlight the dystopian features of the plot – in this futuristic world, people are controlled from birth.

Most of the description in the extract is written in simple sentences, expanded with some detailed information:

Eighty cots stood (in a row) (against the wall.)

These two **prepositional phrases** are adverbial phrases, modifying the verb 'stood', suggesting order and control.

There was a (whisper) (under every pillow.)

This noun reinforces the sense of the influence that the people in control have on the children.

This prepositional phrase modifies the noun and emphasises that no child is missed.

Both these sentences convey detail but remain simple and short. This means that they have an even more shocking effect, as they force the reader to pause and think about the information.

The writer recreates this shock effect later in the extract.

(The Director) pushed back the switch. (The voice was silent.)

Beginning the sentence with this proper noun emphasises the total control the Director has over the children.

This simple sentence reiterates the Director's power and highlights the previous noise of the loudspeaker and the brainwashing content of the lesson.

These short, simple sentences act like spotlights. They highlight that the children are being conditioned en masse by a controlling voice while they sleep.

Can you find any other examples of sentences in the extract that suggest influence and control?

What do better writers do?

Better writers choose sentence structures for effect. They can choose from a range of sentence structures, including simple sentences, expanded with carefully chosen descriptive language, to ensure the reader absorbs information.

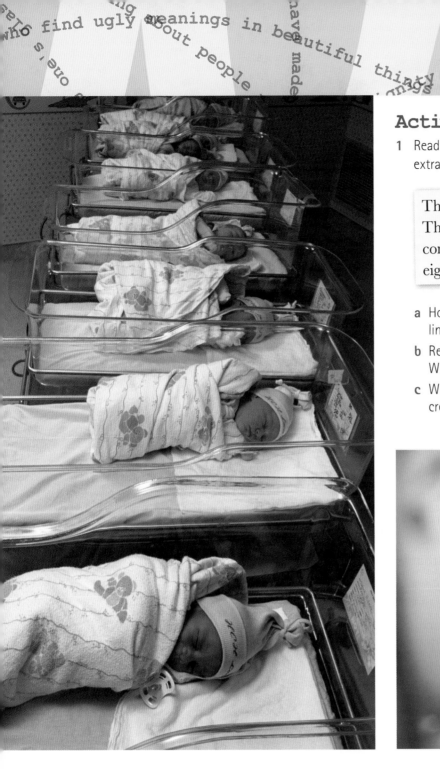

Activity 2

1 Read these three simple sentences from the extract aloud:

> The Director pushed back the switch. The voice was silent. Only its thin ghost continued to mutter from beneath the eighty pillows.

a How could you rewrite these three sentences, linking them into one long sentence?

b Read both versions aloud. Which do you prefer? Write a sentence or two explaining why.

c What effect do you think the writer wanted to create by writing them as three simple sentences?

2 In Lesson 9, Activity 4, you wrote a short text, explaining the values of a society which prized beauty and physical perfection above all else. In the extract from *Brave New World*, eighty tiny children are listening to a text a little like the one you wrote. Imagine a scene in which a group of people are listening to – or reading, or watching – the short text you wrote.

Write a description of that scene. Aim to:

- use dialogue, or a recorded voice, to convey the values which you conveyed in the short text you wrote
- use description to set a scene which, like the scene in *Brave New World*, adds to the impact of this society's values on the reader
- use simple sentences to describe that scene where appropriate, focusing on your choice of descriptive language to develop them.

11 The language of fear

Learning objective

- Understand how writers can create a sense of fear by controlling the release of information to the reader

Many of the worlds you have explored in this unit are controlled by rulers who abuse their power and dominate their people with fear. Dystopian stories often focus on one person who is prepared to stand up to them.

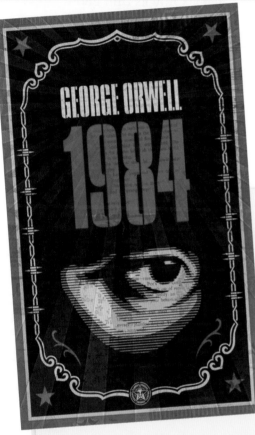

Activity 1

George Orwell's famous dystopian novel *1984* is set in Oceania, a nation brutally ruled by The Party. The leader of this tyranny is Big Brother. The novel tells the story of Winston Smith's attempts to rebel against the power of Big Brother.

The extract below is taken from the penultimate chapter of the novel.

1 Read the extract carefully.

Winston Smith has been arrested. He has witnessed other prisoners being summoned to a place called Room 101 and has watched in alarm as they beg to be spared. Now O'Brien, a senior member of The Party, has summoned Winston to Room 101.

'You asked me once,' said O'Brien, 'what was in Room 101. I told you that you knew the answer already. Everyone knows it. The thing that is in Room 101 is the worst thing in the world.'

The door opened again. A guard came in, carrying something made of wire, a box or basket of some kind. He set it down on the further table. Because of the position in which O'Brien was standing, Winston could not see what the thing was.

'The worst thing in the world,' said O'Brien, 'varies from individual to individual. It may be burial alive, or death by fire, or by drowning, or by impalement, or fifty other deaths. There are cases where it is some quite trivial thing, not even fatal.'

He had moved a little to one side, so that Winston had a better view of the thing on the table.

2 Read the extract again, noting any questions that the text raises in your mind. For example:

- how does everyone know what is in Room 101?
- what is the thing that is the 'worst thing in the world'?

3 What information **does** the writer reveal about Room 101 in this extract?

4 Look again at all the questions you noted down in question 2. Choose three and try to guess the answers, using your imagination and your knowledge of dystopian fiction.

Activity 2

1 Imagine a world of the future, where everyone is expected to live by a set of values and ideals which the authorities ruthlessly enforce. You are accused of failing to live by them. You have been arrested.

2 Write a short extract from a dystopian story in which you describe how the authorities use fear to intimidate you. What might they use to do this? It could be:

- an object • a living creature • something else.

94

WRITER'S WORKSHOP: Creating fear

How can I use determiners and pronouns to create a sense of fear?

In this extract, the writer has very carefully chosen what information he reveals – and what information he does not reveal. Look at this sentence:

> The guard came in carrying a box. He set it down on the further table.

■ This extremely short noun phrase and the indefinite article 'a' leave the reader without information and increase the fear we feel.

■ This third-person pronoun, referring back to 'a box', is used to avoid giving the reader any further information.

The noun phrase 'a box' gives the reader very little information because it does not include any adjectives, adverbial phrases, prepositional phrases or relative clauses. The writer repeatedly withholds information in the extract: the noun 'thing' is used six times, which adds to the suspense through its vagueness.

In other places, the writer chooses to add detail to noun phrases, but even when he does, it does not give the reader much more information:

This pronoun suggests Winston cannot clearly see what the guard is carrying – and neither can the reader.

This non-finite clause gives the reader some limited detail about this object.

> A guard came in, carrying (something) (made of wire,) (a box or basket) (of some kind.)

These nouns and the **conjunction** 'or' reduce the clarity in this description – we cannot make out what this object is.

This prepositional phrase uses the determiner 'some' to make it even less clear.

By the end of this sentence, what is the one thing the reader definitely knows about this object? Why do you think the writer chose this particular detail?

Can you identify any other sentences in the extract in which the writer has intentionally withheld information from the reader? How and why has he done this?

3 In your writing, think carefully about your choice of noun phrases and how you can use them to withhold information. For example, you could:

- use very little description
- choose the little description you use carefully, thinking about what it suggests to the reader
- use determiners and pronouns, such as 'some', 'a', 'something', 'anything', 'somebody', 'anybody', to withhold information.

4 Aim to write around 40–50 words.

What do better writers do?

Better writers carefully control the amount of information they give the reader. They can provide description of settings or objects which they want the reader to be able to picture. They can also withhold description of settings or objects to create specific effects, for example to create a sense of fear of the unknown or unseen.

95

12 Structuring a sense of fear

Learning objective

- Understand how writers can create a sense of fear through the structure of a text

On page 94 you read an extract from *1984*. Winston Smith is in Room 101. A guard has placed an object on a table. O'Brien has warned him that it contains the worst thing in the world. In the paragraphs that follow, the writer reveals more detail.

It was an oblong wire cage with a handle on top for carrying it by. Fixed to the front of it was something that looked like a fencing mask, with the concave side outwards. Although it was three or four metres away from him, he could see that the cage was divided lengthways into two compartments, and that there was some kind of creature in each. They were rats.

'In your case,' said O'Brien, 'the worst thing in the world happens to be rats.'

A sort of premonitory tremor, a fear of he was not certain what, had passed through Winston as soon as he caught his first glimpse of the cage. But at this moment the meaning of the mask-like attachment in front of it suddenly sank into him. His bowels seemed to turn to water.

'You can't do that!' he cried out in a high cracked voice. 'You couldn't, you couldn't! It's impossible.'

'Do you remember,' said O'Brien, 'the moment of panic that used to occur in your dreams? There was a wall of blackness in front of you, and a roaring sound in your ears. There was something terrible on the other side of the wall. You knew that you knew what it was, but you dared not drag it into the open. It was the rats that were on the other side of the wall.'

'O'Brien!' said Winston, making an effort to control his voice. 'You know this is not necessary. What is it that you want me to do?'

O'Brien made no direct answer. When he spoke it was in the schoolmasterish manner that he sometimes affected. He looked thoughtfully into the distance, as though he were addressing an audience somewhere behind Winston's back.

'By itself,' he said, 'pain is not always enough. There are occasions when a human being will stand out against pain, even to the point of death. But for everyone there is something unendurable – something that cannot be contemplated. Courage and cowardice are not involved. If you are falling from a height it is not cowardly to clutch at a rope. If you have come up from deep water it is not cowardly to fill your lungs with air. It is merely an instinct which cannot be destroyed. It is the same with the rats. For you, they are unendurable. They are a form of pressure that you cannot withstand, even if you wished to. You will do what is required of you.'

'But what is it, what is it? How can I do it if I don't know what it is?'

O'Brien picked up the cage and brought it across to the nearer table. He set it down carefully on the baize cloth. Winston could hear the blood singing in his ears. He had the feeling of sitting in utter loneliness. He was in the middle of a great empty plain, a flat desert drenched with sunlight, across which all sounds came to him out of immense distances. Yet the cage with the rats was not two metres away from him. They were enormous rats. They were at the age when a rat's muzzle grows blunt and fierce and his fur brown instead of grey.

'The rat,' said O'Brien, still addressing his invisible audience, 'although a rodent, is carnivorous. You are aware of that. You will have heard of the things that happen in the poor quarters of this town. In some streets a woman dare not leave her baby alone in the house, even for five minutes. The rats are certain to

attack it. Within quite a small time they will strip it to the bones. They also attack sick or dying people. They show astonishing intelligence in knowing when a human being is helpless.'

There was an outburst of squeals from the cage. It seemed to reach Winston from far away. The rats were fighting; they were trying to get at each other through the partition. He heard also a deep groan of despair. That, too, seemed to come from outside himself.

O'Brien picked up the cage, and, as he did so, pressed something in it. There was a sharp click. Winston made a frantic effort to tear himself loose from the chair. It was hopeless; every part of him, even his head, was held immovably. O'Brien moved the cage nearer. It was less than a metre from Winston's face.

'I have pressed the first lever,' said O'Brien. 'You understand the construction of this cage. The mask will fit over your head, leaving no exit. When I press this other lever, the door of the cage will slide up. These starving brutes will shoot out of it like bullets. Have you ever seen a rat leap through the air? They will leap on to your face and bore straight into it. Sometimes they attack the eyes first. Sometimes they burrow through the cheeks and devour the tongue.'

The cage was nearer; it was closing in. Winston heard a succession of shrill cries which appeared to be occurring in the air above his head. But he fought furiously against his panic. To think, to think, even with a split second left – to think was the only hope. Suddenly the foul musty odour of the brutes struck his nostrils. There was a violent convulsion of nausea inside him, and he almost lost consciousness. Everything had gone black. For an instant he was insane, a screaming animal. Yet he came out of the

blackness clutching an idea. There was one and only one way to save himself. He must interpose another human being, the body of another human being, between himself and the rats.

The circle of the mask was large enough now to shut out the vision of anything else. The wire door was a couple of hand-spans from his face. The rats knew what was coming now. One of them was leaping up and down, the other, an old scaly grandfather of the sewers, stood up, with his pink hands against the bars, and fiercely sniffed the air. Winston could see the whiskers and the yellow teeth. Again the black panic took hold of him. He was blind, helpless, mindless.

Activity 1

1   At the beginning of the extract, the writer has described the cage in three long descriptive sentences, increasing in length, followed by a short sentence. What effect does the writer's choice of sentence length have here?

2   How often does the writer use the word 'cage' in this passage? Why has the writer chosen to structure the text in this way?

3 Look closely at this section of the extract:

> These starving brutes will shoot out of it like bullets. Have you ever seen a rat leap through the air? They will leap on to your face and bore straight into it. Sometimes they attack the eyes first. Sometimes they burrow through the cheeks and devour the tongue.'

What do you notice about the last two sentences? What is the effect of this on the reader?

Activity 2

1 Think carefully about the language which the writer has used to describe the rats. Complete the table below.

Nouns	Adjectives	Verbs	Adverbs and adverbial phrases
brutes		shoot	
bullets		leap	

2 Which groups of words do you think are particularly effective at creating a sense of fear for the reader? Which specific words are particularly effective?

3 Choose a short extract of one or two sentences in which the writer describes Winston's reaction to the rats. Complete a table like the one above, identifying examples of the writer's language choice that are effective in describing Winston's fear.

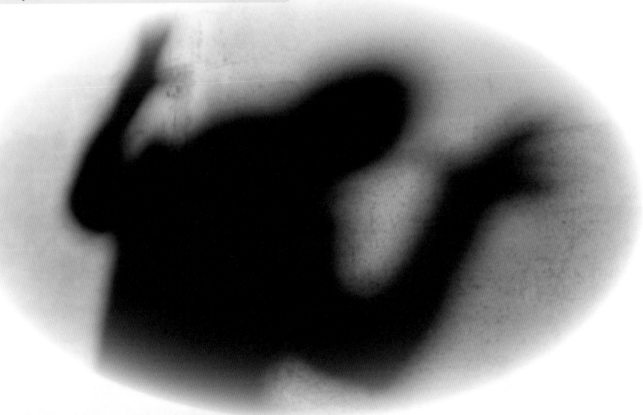

Activity 3

1 Look again at the sentences you wrote in Lesson 11, Activity 2, on page 94. In them you described how the authorities used a frightening object or creature to intimidate you.

2 Now imagine the rest of the scene as the object or creature gets closer. Write 5–10 sentences in which you:

- describe that object or creature getting closer and closer to you
- describe that object or creature, making it as terrifying as possible
- describe your fearful reaction to this creature or object.

You might want to do one at a time, using two or three sentences for each of these sections of your text. Throughout your writing, remember to:

- experiment with the order in which you organise your sentences. How can you structure your writing to create maximum tension and terror for the reader? How do you suggest that the danger is coming nearer?
- use some of the language you identified in Activity 2 and add some of your own.

CHECK YOUR WRITING

➡ Look back at your writing. How successfully have you:

a sequenced your sentences to create tension and terror? Refer to the bullet points above and think about how the structure of your writing creates a sense of fear.

b selected language to describe the object or creature's approach and your reaction to it? You might want to ask a friend if they think you have chosen sufficiently terrifying nouns, adjectives, verbs and adverbs.

➡ Write one or two sentences reflecting on what you have done well and one or two sentences about what you might be able to improve, and how.

13 Planning a dystopian short story

Learning objective

- Understand how to plan a dystopian short story

Activity 1

1 First of all, you need an idea from which your story can grow. Use the questions on this page to gather your ideas, noting them down as you go.

You could start with the setting of your story ...

Will it be set in:

- an entirely strange, unfamiliar future world
- a strangely familiar world, some parts of which your readers will recognise
- somewhere that, at first, seems like a utopia – until the reader begins to notice that all is not as perfect as it seems
- a world which is clearly dystopian from the very beginning of the story?

Your final task in this unit will be to write a short dystopian story. Before you can start writing, you need to gather your ideas. You may want to re-use some of the ideas you came up with earlier in the unit, or you may want to start from scratch. Use the activities on these pages to plan your story.

What will make this world a dystopia? Remember, writers often take a contemporary concern as the basis for a future dystopian world. Will it be:

- a set of values and ideals which dominate society
- a brutal and authoritarian ruler
- a scientific or technological discovery that has changed the way human beings live
- a war or disaster that has changed the Earth forever
- something else?

Or you could start with an idea for the central character or characters in your story.

> Will they be:
> - male or female
> - young or old
> - someone who has grown up this world or a newcomer?
> - someone who has suffered because of the way this society is run, and wants to change things
> - someone else?

Or you could start with an idea for **something that happens in your story.**

> For example:
> - a speech or some kind of broadcast through which you show the reader the values and ideals of this society, like the mayor's speech in *The Hunger Games* extract
> - a terrifying encounter with the powers that rule your dystopian world, like Room 101 in *1984*
> - a scene which shows the impact of this world on ordinary people, like the conversation between Rick and Iran Deckard in *Do Androids Dream of Electric Sheep?*
> - something else.

What do better writers do?

Better writers:

- use the key features of their chosen genre, but try to make their stories original and not copy ideas from other books or films
- plan their stories, thinking about the effect they want each stage of their story to have on the reader
- keep their readers guessing; the reader may think they know how the story will end, but better writers try to surprise them.

Look over your ideas. Which ones do you like? Which ones would work together to create a story? Circle or tick the ones that look promising.

2   What effect do you want your story to have on your readers?

To warn them?   To shock them?   To make them change the way they live?   To frighten them?

To make the world a better place?

Something else?

Write two or three sentences explaining how your story could achieve this.

3   Now you need to structure your story, using the four-part narrative structure:

	What does that mean?	What effect does it have?
1 Exposition	The reader is introduced to the setting, the characters and the situation at the start of the story.	It gives the reader enough information to engage them in the story, making them wonder how it will develop.
2 Conflict	The main character or characters encounter a problem which they must overcome.	It makes the reader want to find out how the characters will tackle such a difficult situation.
3 Climax	The conflict reaches its worst point. It's not just a problem now – it's a REALLY SERIOUS problem.	It leaves the reader unable to work out how the main character or characters can ever solve their problem.
4 Resolution	The conflict is resolved – either happily or sadly.	It leaves the reader feeling relieved and satisfied that the tension of the story has come to an end.

4 Think about what will happen in each of the four stages of your story. You could start or finish with some of the ideas below, or come up with your own. Fill the gaps in the story outlines below. How could these situations develop before they are resolved?

Exposition	Conflict	Climax	Resolution
Our hero lives a harsh but quiet life in a dystopian world – until he or she is chosen for a special task.			Our hero succeeds in his or her task.
A terrible disaster changes the world forever. Our hero must fight to survive – and to save his or her loved ones.			Our hero succeeds – but soon learns that, in this world, nothing is what it seems.
Our hero tries to rebel against the brutal and harsh government that keeps its people living in poverty and fear.			Our hero fails.
Science and technology seem to have created the perfect utopia – until our hero realises that something has gone very wrong.			Our hero fails – and must pay the price for challenging the authorities that control this world.

CHECK YOUR PLANNING

➔ Look back at all the planning for your story. Will the story you have planned:

- use some of the key features of the dystopian genre

- hold the reader's attention

- have a powerful and satisfying ending

- be clear so that the reader understands exactly what is happening and why?

➔ If you answered 'Maybe', 'I hope so' or 'No' to any of these questions, have another think about your plan and what you can do to improve it.

Assessment: Writing a dystopian short story

Learning objective

• Understand how to write a dystopian short story

WRITE

You are now ready to complete the final task in this unit.

Your task

Write a short story in the dystopian genre. Aim to write between 500 and 750 words. Remember to:

• follow the plan you prepared on pages 100–102
• use all the skills and knowledge you have gained and practised in this unit
• think about the decisions you need to make as a writer
• think about the effect you want to have on your reader – and how you intend to achieve it.

REFLECT

1 When you have finished writing the first draft of your story, read it through carefully. Are you pleased with it? Which of the following do you feel you have achieved – and which could you improve?

2 For each of the checkpoints (on the right) you feel you have achieved, write a sentence explaining the effect and impact of your choices.

3 Working on your own, or with a partner, look back at the relevant pages in this unit to remind yourself of the choices you can make as a writer.

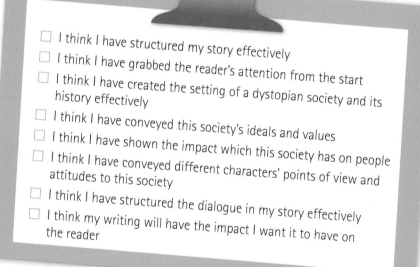

☐ I think I have structured my story effectively
☐ I think I have grabbed the reader's attention from the start
☐ I think I have created the setting of a dystopian society and its history effectively
☐ I think I have conveyed this society's ideals and values
☐ I think I have shown the impact which this society has on people
☐ I think I have conveyed different characters' points of view and attitudes to this society
☐ I think I have structured the dialogue in my story effectively
☐ I think my writing will have the impact I want it to have on the reader

a Now look over your own writing and choose one or two areas which you feel you could improve. For example, this might be:

• varying the choices you make in your writing, such as:

using proper nouns to name the different groups of people in my story

• improving a particular section of your story, such as:

making the scene at the end more frightening and dramatic by thinking about the nouns, verbs and adjectives I use to describe how the main character feels

b Write a sentence or two like the ones above, explaining how you will improve your writing in those one or two areas.
c Make the improvements you want to make to your writing.

103

CHECK YOUR WRITING

➡ Using a different-coloured pen if your story is handwritten, or the comments feature if your story is word-processed, annotate and explain some of your successes. It might look something like this:

> Powerful word choice, placed separately from the rest of the speech to give it emphasis. This shows the Leader's state of mind.

> Proper nouns create the history and details of this society.

'Never,' said the Leader, his voice ringing out from the screen above the crowd, 'since the terrible days of the Hungry Years have we had so much to be grateful for. Every belly and every pocket in this glorious nation is full. Every man, woman and child is healthy and happy. And it is all thanks to the scientific miracle of Varda.'

> Choice of powerful nouns and verbs makes snakes sound terrifying and shows narrator's fear.

> The word 'closer' is repeated to suggest the gradual approach of the snakes.

They writhed and hissed, their tongues flickering just millimetres from her face. She could smell them. Their teeth seemed to drip venom as they edged closer, closer, until she closed her eyes and screamed in terror.

⬇ Looking at the table below, decide which column you think best describes the writing you crafted in this assessment.

I created and described a dystopian society in some detail.	I created and described a dystopian society with some original ideas, thinking about the impact it would have on my reader.	I created and described an entirely original dystopian society in order to comment on my concerns about our own society.
I planned and wrote my story thinking about how it would grab and hold the reader's interest.	I planned and wrote my story thinking carefully about the effect that the characters, action and language would have on the reader.	I planned and wrote my story, creating characters and events and selecting language to achieve my intended effect on the reader.
I used quite a wide vocabulary which I chose for effect.	I used a varied range of vocabulary and sentence structure which I chose for effect.	I carefully crafted my writing, using a wide range of vocabulary and sentence structure which I selected and positioned considering its impact on the reader.